CW00747467

RAW
BEAUTY

Dearest Joanna,

Thank you for your
Raw Beauty and shining it into
my journey, and shining it into
With us both empowering women
the world should watch out!
Much love
Kemi
x.

Published in 2014 in Australia by Kemi Nekvapil
www.keminekvapil.com

Copyright © Kemi Nekvapil 2014
Text copyright © Kemi Nekvapil 2014

Book Production: OpenBook Creative
Cover Design & Typesetting: OpenBook Creative
Editor: Lucy Tumanow-West
Proofreader: Polly Wagstaff
Author photo: Prue Aja Steedman
Cover illustration: Marley Berger

Australia Cataloguing-in-Publication entry

Author: Nekvapil, Kemi
Title: Raw Beauty: The 7 principles to nourish your body, transform your
          mind, and create the life you want

9781925144123 (paperback)
9781925144130 (ebook : epub)
9781925144147 (ebook : kindle)

Subjects: Self-actualization (Psychology) in women.
            Success.

Dewey Number:158.1

The material in this publication is of the nature of general comment only, and does not represent professional advice. It is not intended to provide specific guidance for particular circumstances and it should not be relied on as the basis for any decision to take action on any matter that it covers. Readers should obtain professional advice where appropriate, before making any such decision. To the maximum extent permitted by law, the author and publisher disclaim all responsibility and liability to any person, arising directly or indirectly from any person taking or not taking action based upon the information in this publication.

The content posted here is for informational purposes only and is not intended in any way as a substitute for medical advice, diagnosis or treatment.

RAW BEAUTY

The 7 principles to nourish your body,
transform your mind and create
the life you want

KEMINEKVAPIL

DEDICATION

This book is dedicated to all women who have the courage, commitment and vulnerability to create lives that make a difference not only for themselves, but also for other people and the planet.

RAW BEAUTY

"The contemporary ravages of the beauty backlash are destroying women physically and depleting us psychologically. If we are to free ourselves from the dead weight that has once again been made out of femaleness, it is not ballots or lobbyists or placards that women will need first; it is a new way to see."
– *Naomi Wolf, The Beauty Myth: How Images of Beauty Are Used Against Women*

CONTENTS

INTRODUCTION
About Beauty

Beauty is in the eye of the beholder.
Beauty is only skin deep.
Really?

Then why do only four per cent of women globally* consider themselves beautiful?

The sayings may go like this, but the message women are actually being sold is that beauty is defined by youth, thinness, flawless skin and really, really long eyelashes – hardly empowering for anyone over the age of 30 with a woman's body, the occasional hormonal pimple or wrinkle, and eyelashes she can see through easily.

We women feed multi-billion dollar industries that keep us chasing after a form of beauty that is achievable by a 12-year-old girl at best, and which is an unattainable and destructive myth at worst.

So what do we do, we over-the-hill women? What do we do in these times when a woman is seen to be over that hill so much earlier, and girls as young as 12 are having cosmetic surgery?

It seems we have two choices.

We can decide to have pig fat injected into our faces and our own fat vacuumed from our bodies; to pay for skincare products that actually do more harm than good; we can have our faces cut open, pulled back and stretched around, then sewn up again. Oh, and I forgot the acid peeling – we can burn ourselves as well – on top of decades of dieting (the average woman is on a diet for 31 years of her life).

* Dove Research: *The Real Truth About Beauty: Revisited*

1

This first option is one that many women choose – if you can call it a choice. If age, wisdom and the real female body were cherished in our society, would we even consider these as choices? If kindness, being of purpose and being a worthy human being were valued, would women make these choices for the sake of so-called beauty?

I do not think so. We need to stop cutting, burning, injecting, hiding and starving ourselves. There has never been a better time for women to empower themselves and each other. Imagine if we could stand in our own individual beauty and strength, and if we could then join together to strengthen and empower each other.

Because there is another option…

Raw Beauty

This form of beauty is fuelled by body and mind nourishment. Raw Beauty, once owned by a woman, will nourish her for life; it can never be taken away from her.

No billboard, no magazine, no mass-media hype about the new, improved monkey-dropping juice for anti-ageing can shake her Raw Beauty. Once it has been created and consistently nourished it will transform not only her life, but also the lives of those she touches.

Raw Beauty works on the truth that every woman is beautiful – a given that has been lost through years of societal conditioning and negative experiences. A woman may have forgotten about her unique beauty and stopped expressing it, but Raw Beauty will bring it to life for her again, and encourage beautiful self-expression.

As you are reading this you may not relate to all of what I am about to say, on the other hand, there may be internal light bulbs going off everywhere in your head. As women I believe that at some point in our lives we have all experienced versions of the next few paragraphs.

Whether these behaviours are long behind you or if you are in the thick of it, keep reading.

Some of us need guidance and inspiration in all areas, some in only one or two, but it is beneficial to read them all to understand how they all work together.

THE CURSE OF THE 'NUMB AND DUMB GOOD GIRL'

So many women are wandering around like zombies, drugged up on mind-numbing and soul-destroying tranquilliser drugs. For a whole generation of women it has become the norm to numb and dumb down. It is the norm to feel lost and disempowered, without any sense of self-worth and purpose.

As women we have been duped into thinking we are of no worth unless we are thin, ageless, flawless and good. We have been led to believe that we must please everyone before we please ourselves – that we must be 'good girls' and, above all, likeable.

This need to be liked, and its status as a lifetime achievement of the highest kind, is what stops many women from truly stepping into their deep beauty. As does the related need to please others at any cost, and to never rock the boat.

'Good girls' do not say no, according to this belief system. Instead, they say yes at the expense of themselves, their wellbeing and their dreams.

THE PROBLEM WITH BEING A 'YES GIRL'

Years of saying yes all the time without thinking about our own needs can lead to exhaustion, resentment, resignation, being taken for granted and, eventually, a struggle for our sense of self.

If we do this, we could experience decades of simmering anger underneath our smiles as we say endlessly through our gritted teeth, "Yes, I can do that for you."

'Good girls' do not get angry, though, so only you will know what is bubbling away underneath. And heaven help anyone in the firing line should you ever bubble over.

The truth about women

So let's look at some truths.

Firstly, women are not broken and we do not need to be fixed.

Secondly, we possess an incredible beauty and strength that for many reasons has been hidden.

Personally, I believe that women were burnt at the stake because others felt this was the only way to curtail the awesome power that comes with a woman's beauty and strength. So after this extreme demonstration of what happens to 'bad girls', many of us have not accessed even half of our true beauty and what is possible for us. Instead we have settled for a life in which, we have been told, safety and security should be our ultimate goal. And we have believed it. But I am asking, what about fulfilment, happiness, wellbeing and purpose?

The ineffective fixes

To be 'good girls', we numb and we dumb ourselves down daily in so many ways – by how we speak about ourselves to ourselves, and how we speak about and to each other; and by how we look after our bodies, our environments and our relationships.

Another common way to numb and dumb is through food – food for numbing; food for comfort; food for companionship; and food for control. In fact, food is one of the most widely used forms of self-medication, followed by alcohol.

We women will jump from diet to diet, thinking that losing weight will 'fix' us. But what we fail to do is look at what the weight is protecting us from – the feelings of "I am not good enough" and "I am not worthy". Of course it is hard to lose anything if we feel we are being protected by it. Why would we lose the weight that is making us feel safe?

In addition to drugs and food, we also achieve ongoing numbness by never allowing ourselves to be alone – by avoiding any situation that involves experiencing quietness. Being alone with our thoughts can be very scary because that is where a numbed and dumbed lifetime of pain and resentment lives.

Finding our Raw Beauty

After a lifetime of numbing ourselves in an effort to hide from or deny our Raw Beauty, a quick fix is not the answer. We need to prepare for a process of peeling back the layers to reveal it.

We need to prepare for a journey – which will be a very rewarding one – where every day we will experience a new level of self-respect, self-care and self-nourishment.

And when we get to a place where we can truly honour ourselves and each other, we women can move mountains. Anything is possible.

Let's get started…

1

RAW BEAUTY BASICS

I HAVE SIX important questions to ask you. And then I will talk about eight reasons why we women struggle to nourish ourselves. These will make us think about the value of Raw Beauty and show where the Raw Beauty basics came from and where they can take you.

Take a little time with each question and think about how they relate to you.

Six important questions

1   Do you want a better relationship with yourself?
2   Do you find yourself waiting for everything around you to be perfect before you start living your life fully?
3   Are you struggling with feelings of unworthiness and not being good enough?
4   Do you desire more 'you' in your life?
5   Are you experiencing a lack of fulfilment?
6   Do you desire more joy, passion and purpose in your life?

If you have answered yes to one or more of these questions, read on.

And, firstly, let's deal with the concept of habits.

Release the habit trap

So much of the time we believe we need to change our bad habits to good habits.

If we want to get rid of a bad habit, it is usually suggested we must replace it with a good habit. But that is not always easy. Take giving up smoking, for example. We all know people who have given up smoking, only to replace it with the habit of overeating – so another bad habit replaces the initial bad habit.

Ideally, smokers could replace that habit with a good one – exercise. But I can see why this might not be easy. If you are a smoker, all that is involved is simply getting a cigarette from the packet, lighting it and putting it to your lips. The exercise option, meanwhile, is a completely different kettle of fish – setting an alarm, getting up, getting dressed in gym clothing, going out in the dark and cold, doing things that stress your body and heart (I know smoking does, but you know what I mean), and then getting showered and dressed again, etc.

So replacing a bad habit with a good habit is not always as easy as it sounds, especially when the good habit involves a lot more effort and there is no immediate payoff.

But there is a better option.

Invite the good stuff in

Raw Beauty is not about changing bad habits – I do not even like using that terminology – but about adding nourishing actions to our life.

With Raw Beauty, there is nothing we have to give up unless we desire to give it up along the way. We do not need to completely change the way we live, although some women do just that on their Raw Beauty Journey, and enjoy their lives more because of it.

With Raw Beauty, we will add more and more of what is important to us in small, manageable pieces. We will add more of what makes us happy and more of what nourishes us. And as we do, the non-nourishing habits will begin to fade because they are being squeezed out – not through being forced out, but by creating less and less space for them.

I can tell you with my hand on my heart that in my discovery of Raw Beauty, I have never forcibly stopped myself from doing anything. It just happened that once I started adding more nourishing actions to my life, the less nourishing actions spontaneously fell away. For example, over the past 15 years the following things that previously were completely normal for me have disappeared from my life: drinking coffee and soft drinks; eating a loaf of bread in one day (true, and more than once); eating fast food; drinking too much alcohol every weekend; being around destructive and negative people; experiencing regular headaches, extremely painful menstrual cycles and insomnia; hiding from my fears; and dumbing myself down.

I never consciously decided to stop any of these things – I just got to a point where they had no appeal for me any more, and I let them go.

No forcing. I just let them go.

When we get to a point where we are not fighting something any more, we can allow something else to come in.

We use up so much valuable energy fighting. And instead of fighting, we can create space for kindness.

Are you kind to yourself? Nourishing ourselves is so much better than being unkind to and fighting with ourselves.

Compare the harshness versus the kindness behind the following sentences.

"I must be more disciplined" versus "I am becoming more disciplined every day and it feels great".

"I must be a better mother" versus "I am a good enough mother".

"I must be thinner" versus "I am becoming more comfortable in my own skin".

Raw Beauty empowers us to create a relationship with ourselves that we are proud of.

We all have the capacity to let go of the good to make room for the great.

Eight reasons why we struggle

Now it is time to consider the eight reasons why women struggle to nourish themselves and their lives. Understanding the effect of these reasons will prepare us to begin to let go of them and invite Raw Beauty into our lives.

Read these reasons with your own thoughts, feelings and experiences in mind.

1   We feel not good enough or broken and in need of fixing

This means we are prone to adopt diets that punish us, that we hope will fix us, for example, or we start courses that promise to change our lives in seven days. And when the diet or course inevitably does not work, we are left feeling not good enough – again – and we give up and feel like a failure. Until we decide to repeat the cycle of fixing ourselves again…

2   We confuse diet with nourishment

Do you know anyone who has been on a restrictive diet and felt happy? Not likely or not for long. Losing weight might be easily done, but nourishing our body is something completely different – and many women get the two confused. This is why pre-packaged diet food in plastic trays delivered to your door to be heated in the microwave is a viable business in today's society. We are confused and overwhelmed by all of the contradictory dietary information out there.

3   We are unable to say no

We all love to be of help to others, but if being of service to someone else costs us our wellbeing, we have a problem. If we are unable to say no to other people, family, work, and so on, there is a very good chance that we are unable to say yes to ourselves. The fear of saying no and upsetting someone can be the biggest source of unfulfilment for many women. When we put our needs, desires and dreams aside it never ends well – we will wake up one day saying, "What happened to ME?"

4   We take on too much

We all have full lives and the last thing we need is to bite off more than we can chew. When we take on more than we can handle, we can end up feeling like a failure. If we get overwhelmed and cannot succeed in all we say we will do, this can lead to a victim mentality that impacts not only us but also those around us, and leaves us feeling disempowered and resentful.

5   We have the 'good girl' complex

The need to be liked and validated is human, but if we are overly concerned with what other people think of us we may find ourselves living their version of our life. Doing what is expected, flying under the radar and never stepping out of our comfort zone for fear of failure or judgement is how a 'good girl' survives. But if we do not create anything for ourselves and do not strive for anything, in the end we feel the loss of passion and joy in our lives. We grow up to be good but unhappy women.

6   We are waiting for all of the conditions around us to change

We might think, "When I have lost those 5kg things will be better." "When I make more money, things will be better." "When they change their attitude/policy/opinions, then my life will be better." And when all of those ducks are in a row, we will start to live our lives to our fullest potential. But nothing will line up exactly as we want it to, when we want it to, so we may as well just start to live fully now.

7   We give away our power

Taking responsibility for our own life is where the magic is, yet many of us give away our power to our husbands, children, bosses, parents, families, business partners, etc. We are the only ones responsible for our life, and every action we have ever taken has led us to where we are now. We may not like what life throws at us, but, happy or sad, healthy or sick, we are 100 per cent responsible for how we react to what happens to us. It is time to take our power back and own our life.

8   We think self-care is selfish

We are only just coming out of a time when to do things for ourselves was considered selfish. This way of thinking is hopefully shifting, but many women who are physically and emotionally undernourished still believe that to put themselves first is selfish, uncaring and vain. We worry about what people will say about us if we spend time on our own interests. We are happy to say, "I am so busy at work." But we are not so comfortable saying, "I am busy looking after myself." The truth is, we are of no use whatsoever to ourselves or anyone else if we are sick, exhausted and unfulfilled.

To be able to live a nourished life and embrace our Raw Beauty, we need to begin to let go of these eight reasons that cause us to struggle. They will not disappear overnight, but letting go of these eight reasons will make room for your Raw Beauty to shine and thrive.

And now we can talk about the real thing...

Raw Beauty explained

Raw Beauty is based on the concept that our real beauty comes from who we are and the actions we choose to take – from how we feel about ourselves, how we connect with others, and the difference we all make as individuals.

Raw Beauty is the kind of beauty that every woman possesses.

It is the kind of beauty that we need to nourish within us, for us.

Raw Beauty is different for every woman because we are all diff erent. It is what nourishes us and makes us feel good about ourselves as individuals.

The foundation of Raw Beauty is based on seven basic principles.

7 Principles of Raw Beauty

1 Body Nourishment
Nourish yourself with living plant foods on a daily basis for mental clarity, energy and beauty. Move your body to increase your self-sexiness.

2 Self-Love
Be proud of who you are. Nurture yourself and attend to your needs. Be the best woman you can be for yourself and others.

3 Creative Expression
Create your life and honour yourself by nurturing your creativity.

4 Joy Creation
Joy comes from choosing joy, moment by moment. Practise the art of gratitude.

5 Elevation of Relationships & Communities
Surround yourself with women who will raise you higher and support you to create the life you want to live. And be this person for others.

6 Living Your Passions
Be a full expression of your passions and therefore a full expression of your gifts.

7 Purpose & Contribution
Choose your purpose and then powerfully share it with others in ways that make a difference.

You can discover your own Raw Beauty through these 7 Principles, keeping in mind that it is a powerful form of beauty that cannot be given to us – or taken away, either. This form of beauty cannot be found on the scales, in a dress size, in a surgical procedure or in a jar.

Your Raw Beauty affects others

We are all connected and how we feel about ourselves has a huge impact on the actions we take and on those around us. Raw Beauty is about taking actions that make us feel good about ourselves. If we are tired, overwhelmed, resentful and stressed out, this has an impact on how we communicate and interact with others. It affects all our relationships, from work colleagues and partners to children and friendships.

The positives of saying no

I think one of the hardest things for women is saying no to others so that we can say yes to ourselves.

How many times have you wanted to do something for yourself and then work, study or family has pulled you in another direction and your time has disappeared? When this happens again and again, we get used to it – and feel resentful about it, which can lead to a 'poor me' attitude.

Once we arrive at the 'poor me' place, it becomes harder and harder to find the destination that is self-nourishment, self-love and self-worth. This is because we forget that we have a say in how our life goes. We have the right to say NO.

Filling our own cup

It is when we look after ourselves consistently that we have so much more to give to others. I remember hearing once that if you are giving to others from an empty cup, it is like they are stealing from you because you do not actually have anything to give them.

If we had a choice, none of us would drink from a dry watering hole. We would go and find a drinking hole that was overflowing with water, and life.

We need to fill up our cups.

Raw Beauty is not navel gazing

I firmly believe that our personal inner work is the most important work we can do. I am constantly doing 'my work', but the thing that has made the biggest impact on my life in the past and in the present is taking action.

If I had not made my first bowl of raw salad all those years ago and had just thought it would be a nice recipe to try one day, I would not have made the second or third salad.

It was that first salad that has led me to where I am now.

Insight and light-bulb moments are great, but unless they transform into action, nothing happens.

It is important to take action if we want to make changes.

You may know of people who talk the talk but struggle to walk the talk (and this may be you), but the walking is the action – it is the walking that gets you from A to B.

Decide to deserve it

Who decides what we deserve? Only us.

Do you believe that we deserve to be nourished and feel joyful and passionate about ourselves and our life?

Imagine being passionate about yourself? How would it feel to learn to love yourself as much as you do your most beloved?

A large part of the Raw Beauty journey is deciding that you are worth your own effort, for yourself. You are worth your own commitment.

What is commitment?

The sense of what commitment is changes from person to person. When I say I am committed to something, I mean I will do everything I can to get the results I want for myself or the results that I have promised to someone else.

This is not the same for everybody. Some common ideas about commitment include, "I am committed to exercising if I am not tired", "I am really committed to him – unless it gets too hard", "I am committed – as long as it all goes my way", "I am committed if they are committed", "I meant to be on time, but…", "I am committed to losing weight, but it was rude to say no to the cake and then I was offered a second piece".

Another level of commitment looks like this: "I am committed to exercising regardless of the weather, and I will do star jumps in my lounge room if I have to", "I am very committed to her and it will be up and down, but I am ready", "I am committed because I am committed", "I am always 15 minutes early", "I want to lose weight and I was offered cake so I said no".

This is a great time to look at what your level of commitment is.

Raw Beauty commitment

On a recent Raw Beauty Retreat, one of the participants was really struggling with the idea of commitment. She had set her heart on a particular home that she and her husband were about to buy. A day or two before the auction, her husband got cold feet and decided that it was too risky to buy the property. She then spent three days in bed crying because for her, this property was the exact representation of all she held dear and all she believed in for herself and her family.

She was so committed to creating and nourishing a particular life for her family in this home she had even told her husband, "If we get this house I do not think I will ever want for anything again."

Because they did not buy the house and it was so painful for her, she had unconsciously decided never to commit to anything again.

When we worked through the pain of this experience, she then decided to commit in a huge way. She decided to commit to making the lives of poor Balinese children better, through playful education and experiences.

The past informs who we are now, but it does not have to inform who we are going to be going forward.

This book is here to support you to succeed in creating the life that you want for yourself. For example, you choose your daily Raw Beauty Action in line with what you can commit to. There are no 'shoulds' in this book – I love the saying "Don't should all over yourself". If you already have a full day, take on an action that you know you can achieve on that day.

As you succeed with this, you will increase your self-belief and your capacity to stick with something.

Time for Raw Beauty Action

A nourished body and mind can create a beautiful and fulfilling life, but we have to decide that we are worthy of our own time, that our needs are important and that our own self-nourishment is valid.

When we begin to look at ourselves in this way and start to take small, sustainable actions consistently we begin to live out our commitment to ourselves and our lives, and then wonderful changes can and will occur.

Raw Beauty helps support the creation of an empowering beauty from within that then spills forth into a beautiful, well-nourished, created-on-purpose life.

Raw Beauty is about choosing to take action from a place of creation and empowerment.

If you are looking for something different that you have not seen before, then by reading this book I promise you have found it.

My intentions are that this book will raise you higher with every page turned, that every day you will experience the power of Raw Beauty, and that day by day your self-love, passion and joy will increase. This, in turn, will spread itself in ways that you cannot imagine now.

Raw Beauty can completely transform the way you see yourself and the way you see the world.

Are you ready?

2
MY STORY & ABOUT THIS BOOK

BEFORE I START showing you in detail how to discover your own Raw Beauty, I want to share with you how I came to discover mine. Without wanting to spoil the ending for you, I think you can guess that Raw Beauty comes out as the heroine of the piece – and the story ends with how we can all discover and celebrate our beautiful uniqueness.

My story begins…

I was born in England in 1974 to Nigerian parents.

Like many parents, they thought education was the most important thing. And like so many middle-class Nigerian parents in the 1970s, mine decided to have me fostered in England so I could have the best English education my parents could provide. Which meant that as a baby until I turned 14, I lived with five foster families. I saw my birth mother in the holidays and would spend time with her when she was over from Nigeria.

All of my foster parents were white, and I grew up as 'the only black in the village' for most of my childhood, except there was one other black girl – my sister, three years younger than me.

Apart from one family we landed with when I was 13 years old, my experience of being fostered was a good one.

Number one family

My first foster parents were loving people, all about family and extremely nurturing. We called them Mummy Olive and Daddy Brian. They were mad country and western fans (and, thanks to them, so am I) and we would spend weekends at country and western carnivals being driven around on big trucks with Dolly Parton and Glen Campbell blasting out from huge speakers.

On other weekends we would go fruit picking, filling baskets with apples, pears and berries depending on the season.

I had three older foster sisters – Sharon, Janice and Nicola – two of whom worked at the nearby factory that made Sindy dolls, so I would receive the latest Sindy doll and accessories every birthday and Christmas, which was extremely exciting.

Little did I know that 'beauty' was already being dictated to me.

We sat around the table every night for dinner as a family, eating meals made with ingredients from the kitchen garden and I can honestly say that the years living with Mummy Olive and Daddy Brian were some of the happiest of my childhood.

Except for a short period in the middle – all I can remember is that Prince Charles and Lady Diana got married when we were with another foster family – we lived with Olive and Brian until I was seven, when they could no longer look after us.

The freedom years

We then went to live with Winnie and Jack. Winnie was not the most open or joyous woman but she loved us deeply, and Jack was a very easy-going and loving man.

Winnie hated to cook, which made for some very interesting meals that came from packets and cans. But one Sunday a month, Jack would make Eve's Pudding – a delicious English dish that involved a baked sponge with apples underneath – which was served with custard. Those Sundays were a special time.

We were given such freedom when we lived with Winnie and Jack – the kind of freedom I try and hold for my own children now. We were sent out on the weekends with money for food and drinks and told to come back when the streetlights came on.

We had a great community of friends and enemies – always necessary for a well-rounded childhood, I think. We were allowed to be children, and we learnt to be resourceful, responsible and self-driven.

From good to bad

We left Winnie and Jack when they became too old to be raising teenagers.

My birth mother asked us if we wanted to return to Nigeria with her or stay in England. We wanted to stay – and then things went downhill very quickly in the less-than-nourishing environment provided by Nan, as we called her.

She had seemed to my mother and to us to be the gentle grandmother-type, but this turned out to be not the case.

I am thankful that I was already 13 when we arrived in this destructive and toxic environment – my life would be very different now if I had grown up with Nan from an early age.

Nan lived in the worst street in town – the kind of place that made people grimace when you mentioned you lived there.

Every night I would go to bed wearing pyjamas plus a woolly hat and gloves, a scarf tied tightly around my neck and long socks pulled up over my pyjama bottoms to limit the skin available to be bitten by the fleas that infested my bed, and the entire house. But of course I would still get covered in flea bites, and it became so bad I developed an obsession with checking my bed and skin for fleas all of the time, along with a habit of scratching constantly even when I was not at home. I felt like fleas were constantly eating me. I felt constantly dirty.

Throughout the year my sister and I lived there I was also emotionally abused and sexually molested on a regular basis by Nan's grandson, who lived next door.

There was also a guy called Jim who lived with us. We never really knew what his relationship was to Nan, but to us he was a drunken one-time fireman who would sit in the corner of our living room and shout racist remarks at my sister and me.

I started to experience strange blackouts. Friends told me that I would suddenly start spitting and talking rubbish in a voice that was completely different, and I would slur my words. I would then black out and wake up with a migraine, with no memory of what had happened.

I went to doctors and the hospital for brain scans, as my doctor thought I might have epilepsy, but nothing was found. I now know these episodes were my way of dealing with the circumstances of my life as a 13-year-old in a terrible situation.

MY SAVING GRACE

What saved me was babysitting for a neighbour who was a single mother with five children. I would get £1 an hour for five hours of babysitting, five nights a week. That was £25 a week. I was rich. Actually, I was free. Money gives you choice, and that money would get my sister and me out of that house every weekend.

We would go to Luton, the nearest big town, and I would give my sister £10 to spend while we hung out at the shopping centre. We would eat some junk food, see a movie and walk around until it was time to go home.

We loved it and we thought we were a little bit cool. But we weren't. We were two black girls doing our best to survive a pretty awful situation.

And this was our weekly routine.

One day we returned home to Nan's from spending the holidays in London with our birth mother to find an eviction notice on the front door. Nan was nowhere to be found, and so we went to school not wearing our school uniforms. The deputy headmistress asked us why we were not in school uniform and we told her.

We had nowhere to go and we were officially homeless. Our foster mother had disappeared and our birth mother was now in Nigeria with no idea what was happening to us, and we did not know how to find her.

We were now formally in care.

We slept at friends' houses for a few months, until the day we had an interview with the owner of a local children's home.

Our social worker had asked me, because I was the oldest, if I wanted my sister to go to the foster home they had found for her or for us to stay together and go into a children's home. I chose a children's home so we could stay together, and I believe the owner of that place to be one of the many angels that have appeared in my life.

After meeting us and reading the assessments from our social worker, this man wouldn't give us a place in the children's home because, he said, despite the situation we were in we were both emotionally stable. And, he said, if he took us into the children's home, we would be on drugs or pregnant within a year. I was 14 and my sister was 11.

That was the best rejection of my life and I will be eternally thankful to him for that.

It was heartbreaking for my sister and me to be separated – we were the only family each other had ever really had. And it was around this time that I seriously considered ending my life.

I was 14 and I had had enough. Now my sister was gone. I could not see the point of going on.

Enter three angels

A month or so after my sister went to her new foster family, by chance a place was found for me by Mrs Reardon, my religious education teacher at school. She asked around her church community for a temporary home for a 14-year-old girl until social services could find something more permanent, so Sue and Russell Price agreed, thinking it was going to be for a few weeks. And that is how I arrived at my final foster family, where I was to be given the greatest gift of my life – choice.

I arrived at the Price's house with two plastic bags holding all of my belongings. The parents of a friend where I had stayed had given me some clothes, but I had only the bare minimum.

The following day I went out with Sue to buy clothes, including underwear. She asked me what colour knickers I wanted – pink or multi-coloured?

I did not know what she was asking me.

She asked again.

I asked what she meant.

"Choose," she said. "What colour knickers do you want?"

For the first time in my life I had been given choice.

The lack of choice in my life – having never had a say in where I would live or with whom I would live, for starters – had made a big impact on me. And the empowerment I felt now that I was allowed to make choices was overwhelming. In fact, I became a fully-fledged chooser, and several months after living with Sue and Russell, my blackouts stopped.

My beauty battles

I grew up feeling that I was not beautiful because I was not white and I did not have blonde hair cascading down over my shoulders, like in the hair-care ads.

By the time I turned 16, I started to feel really bad about my life and myself. As a teenage girl, I desperately wanted a boyfriend and I wanted to be thin.

I had put on a lot of weight in a short period of time because I was eating for comfort, and I felt the only control I had in my life was over what I put into my mouth. And I put a lot into my mouth.

I started suffering from bulimia – I would binge and then take laxatives. I did this every day for nearly six months, and then one day after a physical education class at school, I was given another one of the best gifts I have ever received. From where it came depends on what you believe in, but it came. I call messages or insights such as these 'divine downloads'.

I AM ENOUGH

I was looking in the mirror in the changing rooms and I became acutely aware that I did not look like anyone else around me. Of course I had been aware of this previously, but on another level – this was different.

Not only did I suddenly get that I did not look like anyone else, it also occurred to me that I had a completely different life from everybody else – I had different experiences, different highs and different lows. I realised that if I continued to compare myself to my friends, I would never, ever be happy. And neither would I ever feel good enough for myself or for anyone else.

That was it. I stood in front of that mirror and declared to myself, "I will never compare myself to anyone else ever again. I am enough."

I am Kemi

Since that day I have never compared myself to anyone else, and this has served me well.

As I had grown up around white people, the only black people I spent time with were my mother, aunties and cousins during the school holidays. So when I first ventured into acting, I was given a small role in a hip-hop music video and it was a huge thing for me to be surrounded by other black people.

Finally, as a teenager, I was with who I had been told were 'my people'.

But it did not take me long to figure out that I was definitely not 'their people'. According to them I was too posh, I did not speak like them and that was the end of that. A bit of an anticlimax, to say the least.

Okay, to be honest, I was more into *Les Misérables* the musical and the Carpenters than I was hip-hop. And it was in that moment that I realised I did not fit with this particular group either.

Another divine download had arrived: okay, before I am a woman, before I am black, I am Kemi. From now on, I get to decide who I am. No group of people is going to define me – I will define me.

Permission to dream granted

Sue was a careers teacher and so we started planning my future. I decided to leave school at 16 and train as a baker, and then I wanted to audition for drama school. I was a great kneader, and even won the National Hovis Bread Baker of the Year competition and Cake Decorator of the Year between 1990 and 1992, just in case you were interested. And after I left bakery college, I worked as a baker and chef on and off for nearly 20 years.

I was in constant survival mode as a child and had very little time or opportunity for dreaming of the future. After baking college there were more choices to make and dreams to fulfil.

I never imagined drama school was something I would be able to choose, but at 18, there I was, relishing every moment, not taking a moment for granted and grasping every opportunity that arose. Whenever a teacher wanted a volunteer, my hand was up. In fact, it was always up, and one day as I stood straining to get my hand the highest to volunteer for a part yet again, another girl in the class stood up and said, "Kemi, we are all sick of hearing your voice. Just sit down."

Permission to dream withdrawn

I was devastated. No one in the whole room said anything, not even the teacher.

I will never forget that feeling. I felt incredibly alone, vulnerable and humiliated. And because no one else said anything, I believed that they all must have been thinking the same thing – that it must be true.

I sat down.

Then, at a party a few months later, this same girl physically attacked me. And no one helped me – they just watched. I was left lying on the floor, in shock and crying.*

I thought. "Everyone hates me this much."

But my mime teacher, Adam, helped me up from the floor, took my hand, draped a blanket over me and held me as I cried.

* I will say that at that time in my life I was a strict vegetarian and was involved in many a protest march, ranging from stopping cruelty to animals to anti-racism, anti-homophobia and non-violence marches. Because of this, I threw no punches when I was being hit and only defended myself from her blows. If I had not been so politically correct and peace-minded, I would have pulverised her! I just wanted you to know that, for the record.

"This is nothing to do with you," he said. "She has a problem with who you are. This is not about you."

But his words came too late. I had already decided three months earlier, when the "Just sit down" comment had been made, that from then on, my only purpose was to make sure that people thought I was nice. It had been proven to me that if I was too passionate, too excited, too 'me', people would hate me, hurt me, humiliate me and not help me.

So the new me was not too passionate, too threatening, too inspired, too anything. Just nice.

I wanted to be a nice, quiet, good girl.

The new 'not me'

I slowly stopped being all of me, so that people would like and approve of me – and it was exhausting hiding parts of myself to make other people feel comfortable.

I became a prisoner to other people's opinions of me and continued to shut down more and more parts of myself, without even being aware that I was doing it. I was protecting myself from being hurt like that ever again, from feeling that misunderstood and alone.

We do that, us humans — we close down to protect ourselves, and life continues.

For me, my shut-down life as the nice version of Kemi was actually quite exciting. After three years at a top London drama school, I became a successful TV and theatre actor in England. I worked non-stop for seven years and had wonderful opportunities.

While in New York with the Royal Shakespeare Company, I had spent the day with one of the other actors who was telling me how she had wanted to act since she was three years old, and that being here was her dream come true.

That night as I was taking off my make-up after the show, I suddenly realised that although I loved acting, it was not my dream. I was in the world for something else. I did not know what, but I did know that I missed being in a professional kitchen as a chef, playing with food all day.

THE NEED TO LEAVE

It took me 18 months to leave acting. At the start, the pressure I felt from my family and peer group to continue was greater than my desire to leave. Why would I leave? I had a wonderful life — I made great money, I had public respect and recognition.

I was so confused and unhappy.

Why did I not want to continue with this promising career? Was I being stupid? Selfish? Was there something wrong with me?

Soon after, when my good friend Gisella asked me what it was I wanted to do, I told her that all I wanted was to travel the world as a chef and yoga teacher.

About a week later Gisella came running into the café where I was working and told me about a man who was opening a resort in Thailand

and needed a chef. He was in London interviewing people and hadn't found anyone who fitted the bill yet.

She told me to go for it. I did.

We met in a pub and I knew my life would change forever if I said yes to his offer. I also knew not many people in my life would think this was a good idea.

There was no money – actually *no* money – but my food and board would be covered.

I decided to jump.

I also thought if I was going to do this crazy thing, I may as well add more crazy and go to India to train as a yoga teacher.

Jumping to the next level

Telling people that I was leaving a successful and lucrative career as an actor to work for a complete stranger in Thailand for no money made for some very interesting conversations.

My foster father called me a "stupid girl", which cut deeply, but I left anyway. And thank goodness I did because I met my future husband in Thailand, and it was he who introduced me to the concept of raw food.

The authentic me

Whenever I have gone out of my comfort zone, wonderful things have happened. When I started to add raw foods to my life, things started to change – not just my body, but how I felt in my body and how I felt in the world around me.

That was over 10 years ago, and as I get older I feel more beautiful. I am very comfortable with who I am and who I am creating myself to be. I do not hide myself or protect myself anymore (except maybe just a little bit – I am only human, after all) but I certainly never apologise for being me.

I truly believe that I was only put on this planet to be me. The more 'me' I am, the better life gets. And I believe that for every other woman, too. We were all put on this planet for exactly the same reason – to be ourselves.

No hiding.

The more we can nourish ourselves as women, the more we can give to others in a meaningful way.

As we become ourselves, life completely transforms.

CHOOSING OUR BEAUTY

My lifelong commitment is to see that each woman on this earth gets what she wants from life. I want to be a living example of all that is possible when women are empowered and inspired to build a solid foundation for self-love and feeling great about themselves.

My life's journey has not been an easy path – show me someone whose has – but I am incredibly grateful for what it has taught me and where it has led me. I would not change any of it.

What I have learnt from life so far is that choice is our greatest power, and that we are responsible for how we respond to what life throws at us.

People are kind, loving, beautiful and generous – as well as all of the opposites of these.

I choose beauty because I have experienced ugly and I do not choose to live there anymore.

I have learnt that my beauty comes from who I am and the actions I take.

Our beauty is our life, our experiences, our actions and our contribution.

3
HOW THIS BOOK WORKS

BACK IN CHAPTER 1, Raw Beauty Basics, I introduced the 7 Principles of Raw Beauty, which are the keys to this concept and designed to delve into and explode the personal limitations we have put onto ourselves and our life, and possibly the lives of others.

As each of these limiting thoughts and practices is replaced with nourishing and empowering actions, we start to experience ourselves and the world around us in exciting new ways.

How to approach each principle

There is a separate chapter for each of the Raw Beauty Principles. Starting at Raw Beauty Principle 1 – Body Nourishment – each principle, when implemented, naturally leads to the next. For example, when you start to nourish your body with good food, nourishing thoughts and healthy movement follow, you start to love yourself more, allowing an opening for creativity, and so it goes on. So, ideally, they need to be done in order.

I discuss these principles in detail, sharing my experiences and offering my insights and advice. Then a woman will share her story of her Raw Beauty Journey. At the end of each chapter there are several questions for you to mull over and hopefully journal about. After thinking and writing about these questions, you will then choose a Raw Beauty Action to take on that day from the three options I supply.

When you have chosen your Raw Beauty Action, put it into action as soon as possible – ideally on the day you read about it.

STEP BY STEP

I highly recommend you approach this book in a step-by-step fashion, putting the Raw Beauty Actions into action as you go along, and before you proceed to the next Raw Beauty Principle. In other words, only read one principle at a time and do not read the next principle until you have taken your action.

If you read the whole book without committing to any of the Raw Beauty Actions, which all build upon each other as you go along, you will miss 95 per cent of what this book is about.

DAY BY DAY

The concept of Raw Beauty is based on these small, sustainable actions that you choose and that you can do consistently when needed. All of the Raw Beauty Actions elevate you and your life in some way.

For each Raw Beauty Principle there are three Raw Beauty Actions that you can choose from to enhance your experience of you and of your life.

Many of the Raw Beauty Actions will take between 10 and 30 minutes, so you will need to choose one that works with what the day already holds for you.

SHARING IS GOOD

When you are putting the Raw Beauty Actions into practice, please share them with other women in your life – women who do not see themselves as beautiful, who are not living the lives they want, who give too much to others and take nothing for themselves, who find it hard to take time out. Feel free to share the Raw Beauty principles and actions.

Our beauty is ours to own. When we truly own it, we can share that understanding with others so they can see how beautiful they are, too.

It's your journey

As you work through this book, which is in the form of a workbook, take a moment or 10 to be present to what small shifts and changes you can add to your life right now.

This is not a quick fix. This is about taking small, consistent actions – and some really big scary ones, too.

I want to show that you can add these actions gently and gradually without overloading your busy life; the aim of this book is not to add more 'shoulds', but to add more 'you' to your life.

So, as you work through this book and discover Raw Beauty remember this is your journey. Remember that you already have everything you need to powerfully step into who you are – it's just that maybe the demands of life have been hiding that from you.

Avoid the 'on Monday' trap

When we are inspired, we want to change and shift everything in our lives at once. "On Monday I am going to…" (fill in the gap). We all know how well those declarations to change our lives 'on Monday' never work – exciting to contemplate but hard to actually maintain. At best you are inspired by a new beginning; at worst, if it does not happen or 'fails', you are left feeling worse about yourself.

This is all about you

The 7 Principles of Raw Beauty are about you feeling good about yourself, so that you can go out into the world and do what you were put here to do – shine!

Step into yourself – all parts of yourself – and you will be amazed at what you find and how truly beautiful you are.

Asking for permission

Do we need to ask for permission to raise our level of self-care and self-love? The answer is, yes. And the person we need to ask permission of is ourselves.

Many of us have spent so long putting our needs, desires and dreams on hold for 'one day', we actually need to ask for permission to nourish our needs, desires and dreams now. And the beautiful thing about giving ourselves permission is that it releases the eternal guilt that many women feel – guilt for taking time for ourselves, guilt for doing things for pleasure, guilt for saying no to another's needs so that we can nourish our own.

This is not necessarily easy, though. Like anything we want to shift in our lives, it takes time to form new habits. But unless we start, it will never shift.

The inner voice that is the owner of our negative self-talk will have something to say about our choice to start putting ourselves first: Who do you think you are? You do not deserve it. You are not worth it. You will fail like you always do. You are selfish. People will talk about you.

I have a secret to share with you – most people on this planet have the same voice to deal with every day. Some people manage to quieten it, slow it down, ignore it or have gained tools to manage it, but all of us have it.

I have it. And I actually find it freeing to know it is a common part of the human experience – and all we can do is gain tools to manage the voice, and sometimes we need to take action in spite of the voice. Plus, the more action we take to build our self-care and self-love, the less hold the voice has over us.

Choosing your Raw Beauty Actions

Remember, when choosing your Raw Beauty Actions, take one small step at a time. Overwhelm is not allowed. There is nothing to prove – you deserve it and you are worth it.

So it is time to commit to yourself as the most important person in your life – not in a selfish way, but in a self-appreciative, self-respecting, 'self-filled' way.

When we say 'yes' to ourselves, we are saying 'yes' to our lives.

4

PRINCIPLE 1
Body Nourishment

Nourishment nugget
*If you want to achieve anything in your life,
you need energy.*

NOURISH YOURSELF WITH living plant foods on a daily basis for mental clarity, energy and beauty. Move your body often to increase your 'self-sexiness'.

The foundation principle

This first principle is the one that feeds all the other six principles. Without it, the others could not be.

It is the foundation for how we feel in life. We experience the power of body nourishment when we feel good, have energy and think clearly. Our actions in the area of body nourishment affect the way we experience all other aspects of our life.

The spin of thin

According to an old, old proverb, early to bed and early to rise makes a man healthy, wealthy and wise – but not so much for women in contemporary life, where 'health' means many other things. And one of the biggest lies we are told is that 'health' equals 'thin'.

Women today pursue thinness at the expense of so much. But if we can shift this view of what health and wellbeing looks like, we can begin to empower ourselves and make better choices, and take more nourishing and sustaining actions.

If you have ever been on a diet – and most women have, at least once – do you remember those days as being the best of your life? Do you recall being full of energy? Did the food deprivation have you wanting to jump out of bed in the morning?

I went on a diet only once. I was in my mid-teens and I think I lasted a week. I hated being told what to eat. All I thought about was when my next meal was coming. Weighing out the food and counting calories took the joy out of eating for me. And I love to eat.

I believe one of the reasons women go on diets is because they think there is something wrong with them that needs to be fixed. This thought process goes beyond a belief that there is something wrong with being overweight. It extends to a belief that there is something fundamentally wrong with us.

In this state of mind, every action comes from a disempowered place of non-worthiness. We may find ourselves miserable, irritable and obsessed with when our next meal will be coming, and what we are going to eat so we do not 'blow the diet'. We are only focused on food and the scales; the scales become our best friend and our worst enemy – if they say what we want, we have a good day, but if they do not, our day is over.

When the scales trigger the feeling of failure, we carry that negative energy with us wherever we go that day. Or we think, stuff it, it is too hard, may as well eat a packet of biscuits or two. This typically makes us feel even more unworthy and so the cycle continues, heading for the next new, improved diet that rolls around.

The well-nourished alternative

For me to feel like a fully authentic version of myself, I could not cut out foods I love – that would make for a very unhappy Kemi. I eat what I want but because I love feeling good, that does dictate my choices. The food also has to taste great to me, and be of a high quality.

Working as a professional chef for all those years, especially with organic and seasonal produce as part of my ethos, my taste buds got spoilt, and I see this as a gift, not a hindrance. I have a raw-inspired way of eating, and I also have a love for many other foods and 'foodie' experiences.

When I started to nourish my body with living food, everything changed. But my definition of nourishment is not a bowl of sprouts. (I could not think of anything worse than having to eat just a bowl of sprouts.) In fact, it falls into two categories for me – food that nourishes us nutritionally, such as raw foods and wholefoods, and food that nourishes us because of our culture, experiences and personal preferences.

My experience, and that of my clients, is that when we start making changes with food and know we are eating in balance (for ourselves as individuals), and we start to move our bodies in a way that we love, we start to feel good. We have more energy, and we think more clearly.

We also start to spend less and less time pulling ourselves apart in front of the mirror, and more and more time focusing on the world outside and bigger issues. How can I be the best version of myself on all levels?

What do I want to contribute to the world? What beauty do I have to offer to the world?

So much more fulfilling than worrying about the size of our bums!

When we decide not to diet, we are committing to a longer, more sustainable process of increasing our health and wellbeing – one that brings joy and empowerment. And that is when major shifts can occur.

The fuel matters

How we fuel our bodies determines how we fuel our lives. Based on this understanding, the principle of Body Nourishment is about sustainable actions that build up your body on many levels and nourish your whole being.

This is the antithesis of dieting. This is about adding empowering actions to your life – ones that are sustainable, life-enhancing and joyful.

As a teenager, I put on a lot of weight very quickly. I was having some of the worst times of my life and the only way I could cope was to add some extra padding to shield myself from the pain. Of course, I did not know it at the time but, in hindsight, that is what the weight gain was about. And I am sure I am not the only one who has gone or is going through this. At the time it was the only thing I felt I had any control over in my life.

Then, in my early 20s, when a relationship of five years ended, I remember internalising everything to such an extent my headspace got really bad. I was working with the Royal Shakespeare Company at the time, and we were all offered free membership at the local gym.

I thought to myself, I can either sit here in devastation or I can do something. So I joined the gym and, from the moment I felt the sweat start to build as I walked the treadmill, I loved it. After that I was at the gym nearly every day, alternating between classes, weights, swimming and the sauna – and what a revelation the sauna was!

Exercising had become my hobby; it made me feel good about myself, and every day my broken heart got stronger. I still allowed myself time to grieve, and there were big bouts of sobbing, but while I was grieving I upped the self-nourishment.

As well as this, I had been practising yoga for a few years, and was on my mat every day healing my mind, body and soul.

My raw food journey

When I first heard about raw food I was shocked. I thought the idea of it was completely ridiculous. Why would anyone want to live on carrot sticks when there was pasta in the world? I remember thinking what sad lives these raw food people must lead.

Later, when I was working as head chef in London's first organic restaurant, a couple would come in and order just a plate of salad greens – no dressing, no nothing. We were quite rude about them and called them 'The Rabbits'.

It turned out the woman had been diagnosed with cancer a few years earlier and was given only months to live. She had converted to a 100 per cent raw diet and she was still alive years after doctors told her she would no longer be around.

So then my thoughts about raw food shifted to, okay, it makes sense that if you were sick you would eat it...

After I met the boyfriend who would become my husband, he gave me a book about raw food that got me thinking again, and the idea actually started making sense. So I added a really large salad to my days. Not a garnish disguised as a salad, but a mega salad with lots and lots of vegetables, dried fruits, nuts, seeds and a juicy dressing.

After only a few days I felt fantastic. The first thing I noticed was that my energy levels skyrocketed. The next thing I noticed was that my bowels were working better than they ever had before. We underestimate how important this is, but our health and wellbeing are dictated by the food that goes into our mouth and also what comes out of our bodies. When we are physically blocked up, we are emotionally blocked up, too.

To be able to release the physical and emotional blockages in this way gave me a new sense of clarity and lightness. And the other major shift I felt in that first week was how deeply I was sleeping. I actually did wake up wanting to jump out of bed and start the day.

The power of raw foods

This is how powerful raw foods are – they add life to our body and do extraordinary things to our mind and spirit, too.

At the end of that first week I remember thinking that maybe this was how I was supposed to have been feeling all my life. I felt like I was experiencing myself on another level – a higher level.

At this point I had not changed anything else in my diet; I had just added more raw food, and not even that much, really – just one great salad to begin with.

When I started my raw food journey, I had no idea what I would gain from it. Of course, I am extremely grateful for the energy, clarity, weight stabilisation, healing, wellbeing and levels of health it has given me. But as a woman, the biggest gift has been an incredibly heightened sense of self, self-love and my purpose in the world.

Women are not told we can feel better and better, but it is true, we can; we just need to know how. And between the low carb, the sugar free, the fat free and the fibre plus, we have simply lost touch with the joy of food.

Mother Nature is a wise woman – which is why she got the job! She created a menu fit for a queen, and the closer we stick to her fresh menu, the better we will feel and look, and the higher the level of self-healing.

Raw food can be the doorway to self-love – it certainly has been for me, and for many of my clients.

When we eat raw foods in quantities that work for us as individuals and nourish ourselves, we feel good about ourselves. When we feel good, we take different actions. And it is once our actions change that our life starts to shift in the direction we want it to go in.

The simplicity of food

Food is not complicated – it really is not. A really simple approach to food is, if it grows, scoff it down!

This book is about Raw Beauty, but if you enjoy a piece of chocolate cake, allow yourself to enjoy a piece of chocolate cake – home-made preferred. There is no point in denying yourself something you want. You will have it anyway (binge, anyone?) but in a less joyful and nourishing way.

The food journey concept

I have used the concept of the 'food journey' for many years. Women on my programs find it frees them from negative self-talk about food, as they can let go of the 'good food' versus 'bad food' concept.

A food journey is simple – it is a path. And it is an individual path – not one food journey looks the same as another, and ours will change as our circumstances change. There is no wagon to fall off and therefore no version of us in the gutter having fallen off the wagon, covered in chocolate-flavoured guilt.

On a food journey you can change the course if you choose – you can turn left or right, and you can come back to your original path when you want.

My food journey goes something like this. I eat a certain way when I am at home, raw food being at the centre of the food journey I have created. When I travel for work and I know I will be staying in hotels, I always take my food basics with me. These basics are a raw seed cereal (which tastes better than it sounds), nut butters, dates, raw bars and green powders. Sometimes I'll also take a pre-made salad dressing and seasoning, and a big container with a lid for mixing and storing food.

When I arrive at my destination, I find the nearest organic grocer and stock up on bananas (which I cannot live without), seasonal fruits, some easy to prepare vegies like carrots, pre-washed greens, cherry tomatoes and olives. Depending on my want, I may also buy some sustainable tinned fish, and away I go.

Some may think that is a lot of work for two days' worth of meals, but I do not agree. I am committed to feeling good and when I leave my food choices in the hands of a hotel, chances are I will end up not feeling so good. So when I am staying in a hotel room for work, I believe it is part of my contract to be the best I can be. This is how the food journey works – I could just as well have turned left off the path for those two days and returned when I got home (and sometimes that may be the case), but travel is part of my work and I want to feel the best I can.

Raw food 101

Although there are many different schools of thought on how best to incorporate more raw food into the way we eat, I go for the simple and individual approach – add as much raw food as works for us as individuals, taking into account our eating habits, culture and lifestyle. There are no hard and fast rules – it's just a case of experimenting and seeing how you go as an individual. However, I do always recommend the Green Smoothie to my clients as the easiest way to start adding more raw foods to their life.

The Green Smoothie (see the recipe for my version below) is a power-packed life-giving gift from Mother Earth's table, and you'll be surprised how much difference adding this one drink can make to your life. In fact, I guarantee you will be left wondering how you ever lived without them once you start drinking Green Smoothies regularly.

Made from fruit, greens and water, the Green Smoothie has thousands, if not millions, of variations. My basic Green Smoothie recipe for beginners follows. If you have issues with fructose, you can make your smoothies with more greens than fruit, and use fruit with less fructose, such as citrus and berries.

Kemi's Basic Green Smoothie

SERVES 2

2 bananas (fresh or frozen)
2 oranges, zest removed,
pith in place
2 handfuls greens, such as spinach,
silver beet, parsley or kale
1 celery stick
3 cups water

Blend all the ingredients in a powerful blender, such as a Vitamix, until smooth.

Depending on how fresh the ingredients are, a Green Smoothie can keep for two to three days in the fridge.

When you drink your Green Smoothie, sip rather than gulp it – your stomach will not be happy if the entire glass hits at once. It is also not a good idea to drink your smoothie after a meal, and especially after a cooked one. Once again, your stomach will not be happy. And if you want to have your Green Smoothie in the morning, I recommend you wait at least 20 minutes before you eat any other form of breakfast on top of it. After a while your Green Smoothie may be all you want for breakfast.

So that is all you have to do – add a Green Smoothie every day. It is a small and sustainable step.

Letting more raw food in

One of the magical elements of adding more raw food to our lives is that after just a few days, our bodies want more. We will be attracted naturally to other living foods, and the foods that we know do not serve our body or mind will slowly start to drop off our radar.

This is a very different approach to cutting out all of the foods that we love or demonising a particular food group.

When we add more raw food consistently, we do not need to make ourselves fight the craving for nutrition-free food – that kind of food just does not appeal anymore or, if it does, we choose a better-quality version or eat less of it.

Nourishing our body and mind

Not only is it important how we nourish our body with the food we eat, we also need to look at how we think while we are eating.

Each of us has particular dishes or foods that nourish our souls in ways that a plate of salad never could. My mother's Nigerian stew will nourish me on levels a Green Smoothie could not come close to. And my mother-in-law's spinach rolls are a miracle that has been nourishing the Nekvapil family for three generations, and will do so for many more, I hope.

Our cultural and personal loves weave together to become our own glorious food tapestry, which we need to honour. Such cultural food traditions are very important. So if your grandmother's chocolate cake has been made for you with love since you were a child, why would you demonise yourself for eating it?

Remember, there is no such thing as good food and bad food, there is just food. Some food makes us feel really, really good and some food makes us feel really, really awful. We need to let go of the idea that when we eat 'good' food we are 'good' girls and when we eat 'bad' food we are 'bad' girls. Keep in mind we are on a food journey – we are allowed to take a left turn sometimes, and it doesn't make us evil. We are humans walking a path.

Create your food journey with joy, happy experimentation and nourishing actions.

Recipes

Here are some of my favourite, simple recipes to bring raw food into your life and onto your table – a delicious breakfast, a couple of fabulous salads and dressings, and a wonderful sweet treat.

Creamy Muesli *with* Honey Almond Milk *and* Prunes

SERVES 2

½ cup raw almonds
2 cups water
1 tbsp honey
¼ tsp nutmeg
2 cups oats
6 whole prunes
Honey, to drizzle

Blend almonds, water, honey and nutmeg in a blender until combined; you now have almond milk.

Place oats in a bowl, add almond milk and mix well. Divide mixture between two bowls. Scatter over prunes and drizzle with honey.

Dream Beauty Bowl

There are no hard and fast rules with this recipe – let your ingredient choices depend on what is in the fridge, what is in season and how you are feeling.

SERVES 2

1 cup mixed raw vegetables, chopped or grated
1 cup salad greens, shredded
½ cup fresh herbs, chopped
1 handful raw nuts and/or seeds
½ cup dried fruit, such as sultanas, currants, apricots, figs

DRESSING
¼ cup olive oil
2 tbsp lemon juice, lime juice, vinegar or mustard (acid component)
1–2 tbsp honey, apple concentrate, maple syrup or date paste (sweet component)
¼ tsp spice, such as curry, cinnamon or nutmeg
Sea salt and black pepper, to taste

Place all the ingredients in a bowl and combine with your hands. Lick your fingers, crunch and get beautiful!

Minty Cauliflower Tabouli

SERVES 2–4

1 large bunch parsley, roughly chopped
½ cup trimmed and roughly chopped cauliflower
½ bunch mint, roughly chopped
½ roughly chopped salad or spring onion
1 cup finely diced tomato or quartered cherry tomatoes
½ cup olive oil
½ cup lemon juice
2 garlic cloves, crushed
Sea salt and pepper, to taste

Pulse the parsley, cauliflower, mint and onion in a food processor until well combined. Transfer to a bowl and add the remaining ingredients. Combine well with your hands.

Beetroot *and* Parsley Salad *with* Fig *and* Lemon Dressing

SERVES 2

2 cups freshly grated beetroot

2 cups finely chopped parsley

DRESSING

½ cup olive oil

Zest and juice of 1 lemon

4 dried figs, stalks removed

To make the dressing, blend all the dressing ingredients in a blender until smooth.

Place the beetroot and parsley in a bowl, pour over the dressing and mix with your hands until well combined.

Lick your hands clean, serve and enjoy!

Beauty Bliss Balls

MAKES 18

1 cup raw macadamia nuts
½ cup cacao powder
Zest of 1 orange
Pinch of cayenne pepper
3 drops vanilla extract
Pinch of sea salt
1 cup Medjool dates, pitted
18 whole dried cranberries

Process the macadamias, cacao powder, orange zest, cayenne pepper, vanilla and salt in a food processor until the mixture resembles fine breadcrumbs. Add the dates and pulse until well combined.

Gently squeeze a small amount of mixture into a ball, approximately the size of a 20 cent piece (no bigger). Push a cranberry into the centre and form the ball around it.

Happy beauty bliss!

Note: You can share these with your friends if you wish, but I wouldn't!

For more recipes please visit *www.keminekvapil.com*

Body movement

With our increased energy levels and mental clarity thanks to the raw foods we are eating, we are going to want to move our bodies and increase our levels of self-sexiness.

We all know that exercising is part of maintaining a healthy body, but what it can do for our emotional wellbeing and personal growth can be the best gift of all. As we dance, run and walk all of our happy hormones are dancing, running and walking, too. Body movement is also a quick way to release stress.

I was out running the other day, when someone doing push-ups to the side of the path shouted out, "What are you training for?" My reply was, "Nothing but my emotional wellbeing." And it can be that simple.

For so many people, the prospect of moving their body goes into the too-hard basket. We create so many reasons not to do it – the children, the partner, the cost, the back, the time… But when we are committed to ourselves and feeling good and nourishing ourselves becomes a priority, we work out a way to do it.

I have run up and down the steps of a train station for 20 minutes at midnight; got my children to design me assault courses on our street, and joined a gym that I would never go to again on the spur of the moment because I needed to de-stress, now! Do not underestimate the power of moving your body and your cells around.

Moving your own way

It is a fact that we feel better on so many levels when we move our bodies. However, I am not talking about having a hard and fast exercise plan that we do only because we have to, when in fact we would rather gouge out our eyes with a spoon.

This is also not about setting ourselves up to fail by declaring that we will run 10km five times a week when we have four children and the last time we ran was when we were in a nappy.

We feel good about ourselves when we set goals and take actions that are achievable. Once those are achieved, we can then raise the bar and up the level of the goal. For example, it will increase our health and wellbeing so much more to walk for one hour three times a week consistently, than to walk for three hours once a month.

This is about choosing ways in which we can move our bodies regularly that actually excite us, preferably four to six days a week. We can make it up ourselves. We just have to love what we do, and then do it.

If we set ourselves up in a routine and then we cannot go for our run or go to our class for whatever reason, we always need to have a plan B up our sleeve. This is where the stair-running and neighbourhood assault courses come in. Or dancing around the house to loud music for 10 minutes; it is extremely enjoyable, it lifts the mood (and possibly the mood of anyone else watching) and will raise our energy levels for the day.

Being accountable to someone or something will also increase the likelihood we will move our bodies often. There is nothing like making an arrangement with a friend and fitness coach, booking in for a class or signing up for a run or walk. We pay the money, we tell everyone we are doing it and generally we are too proud to back out. We also know that if we do not train, it will not go well. So we train and we get committed.

I find my children are the best at keeping me accountable. Once I tell them I am going to do something, I make sure I do it. One reason is because I want them to have a mother they can trust and, secondly, I want them to see that setting goals, working hard and achieving them is a very fulfilling and exciting way to live.

But if you are just having one of those days where there is absolutely no way you are going to be able to move your body, then let go. No self-loathing or 'I am a failure' monologues. Just let go. Tomorrow is another brand new day.

No one else is responsible for your health. You are the only one who gets that job, so honour yourself enough to take it seriously.

Skin food

Once we start to nourish our bodies with joyful eating and increase our self-sexiness through body movement, we start to ask questions about how to nourish our bodies externally.

We are bombarded with the next new super mascara, shampoo and anti-ageing cream, but the majority of these products are filled with harmful ingredients. This would not matter if we only used these products once in a blue moon, but the average woman leaves the house in the morning with 200 chemicals on her body. Many have not been tested, and most have not been tested in the various combinations in which we may be throwing them together. We become the guinea pigs.

If we only wear make up once in while, we may not want to worry about it. But if we use it every day it may be best to change what we use. Products we use every day, like shampoo, conditioner, toothpaste, face cream, deodorant and body lotion are worth investigating.

To go into this in depth would involve writing a whole other book, but since our skin eats 99 per cent of what we put onto it, I ask you, would you eat your shampoo? Empower yourself by doing some research into the brands you use. It is not their job to keep us healthy; their job is to sell as much product as they can and make a profit. It is our job to keep us healthy.

If you choose not to spend the time researching these products, there is a quicker option – find products that are 100 per cent human and planet friendly. These brands tend not to have the huge advertising budgets of the big guns, but your local health food store will have already done the searching for you and found some wonderful products.

But since not all companies are as truthful as others, a little personal research will go a long way.

RAW BEAUTY JOURNEY
Renai, 38 years
Mother of three, stepmother to three and teacher

I had always felt like the ugly duckling. I had listened to negative comments and disregarded the positive. I had spent my teenage years counting calories and berating myself for eating. I remember a day in Year 12, walking to school and working out that if I walked to school and ate three apples for the day, I would definitely lose weight.

I felt like a princess at my deb ball but after seeing the photos, I cried myself to sleep because I truly believed I looked fat and disgusting.

I have since revisited those photos... I looked beautiful! I am sorry for the time I spent despising who I was.

In August 2013, my sister bought me a ticket to Kemi's weekend retreat. I was excited because I had been researching raw food and was looking for quick and easy recipes.

As we stood in the registration queue I was scanning the room, trying to find someone who was bigger than me and who looked sadder than me. I did this everywhere I went. I can honestly say, hand on my heart, that day was the last time I ever did that again. I don't think the same way now. My life was transformed that weekend. There was a change in me and I could see joy in my eyes.

Kemi ran onto the stage and I knew this was a turning point in my life. I learnt about how food impacts my mood and emotions. I learnt about how to use food to nourish my body and soul. Green Smoothies have become a staple. My body craves them and I can almost feel my blood sending me love as the nutrients hit my blood stream.

Body movement is an area I struggle with. It is a constant goal for me to involve more movement throughout my day. I chase toddlers around and by 7pm I am exhausted. Kemi taught me to put in small, achievable goals and to celebrate every milestone. It is an unbelievable feeling when I come to the end of the day and the treadmill has not beaten me!

Kemi teaches about the 7 Principles of Raw Beauty. For me, they are the compass points of my life. When I am feeling in a rut, unmotivated and off balance, I return to my compass points to steer me in the right direction – to regain my bounce and live the life I deserve.

My relationships have improved. I communicate more openly and am comfortable to share my thoughts and ask for what I need. I have created a network of women who inspire me every day.

My life will never be the same as before I became a Raw Beauty Queen. I have the tools to live an inspired, nourished and exciting life. To live anything else is just laziness. Kemi has motivated me to live the best life I can. And I choose JOY!!!

Body Nourishment Questions

1   Do you need to shift your focus from dieting to body nourishment?

2   Could you be kinder to your body?

3   What would you do with increased energy?

RAW BEAUTY ACTIONS

Which one can you add today?

1   Add a Green Smoothie to your day.

2   Move your body in a different way this week.

3   Add more greens to your plate today.

So now you have begun to nourish your body, what happens next?

5
PRINCIPLE 2
Self-Love

> Nourishment nugget
> *Love yourself a little more each day – the rewards
> are immeasurable.*

*BE PROUD OF who you are. Nurture yourself and attend to your needs.
Be the best woman you can be for yourself and others.*

Truth, lies and body love

Here is the truth: YOU ARE BEAUTIFUL!

Here are the lies: You are only beautiful if you are thinner, whiter, younger, richer, cleverer, taller, bigger/perkier breasted, blonder, had less cellulite, and all that.

So if the truth is the truth, why do we spend so much time believing the lies? When you read a trashy woman's magazine, how does it make you feel about yourself? Do you explode with self-love? When you go to bed at night, do you look in the mirror knowing you have added beauty to the world just by being you?

Self-love can be described in many ways, but for a woman on the path of Raw Beauty it means you are consistently taking actions that enhance who you are, as well as taking actions that expand and nourish who you want to be.

Taking action

There is work to do when it comes to creating a high level of self-love. We definitely need to include looking inwards, looking into the past and understanding what has influenced our thoughts, habits and views of the world. But as I mentioned earlier, the way to shift anything is to take regular, consistent action that will change how we feel about the world and ourselves. It is not enough to know why we do all the things we do.

We can stand in front of a mirror pulling at our bodies and literally killing ourselves with our thoughts, or we can change the way we eat, live and think. We can keep complaining about where we work, or we can find a way to leave.

I promise that taking action will make us feel better about ourselves.

Non-action traps

It is interesting to think that we tolerate unhappiness for ourselves much longer than we would allow other people we love to tolerate it for themselves. But the real killer is when the situation we are in is somehow tolerable – when it is not so bad that we feel leaving or doing anything is unnecessary. It is okay. It pays the rent. It is not so bad that we have to take action. And it is in this situation that a shift to self-love will bring a realisation that will fuel action.

The nature of self-love

The journey to self-love can be a lifelong one, depending on where you are starting from and what your childhood was like. Were you validated and elevated as a child, for example, or were you shamed and disregarded? In either case, I know from personal experience that however you get there, self-love is the foundation for a fulfilled and authentic life.

How we feel about ourselves affects everything we will ever do – it affects our relationships, our dreams, where we go, who we surround ourselves with and, most importantly, the actions we take.

Your love for yourself will dictate how you love others.

How you love yourself will teach others how to love you.

This is important.

Not narcissism

One of the most prevalent misconceptions we need to smash is that self-love is arrogant and in some way rules out loving others. Not so.

"Loving yourself... does not mean being self-absorbed or narcissistic, or disregarding others. Rather it means welcoming yourself as the most honored guest in your own heart, a guest worthy of respect, a lovable companion." – *Margo Anand*

Imagine welcoming yourself as an honoured guest in your own heart. Wow.

The feel-good approach

We all have particular actions that make us feel really good about ourselves when we do them. They may be to do with the food we eat, the people we spend time with, the books we read or the places we go.

And when we allow ourselves the time to have these things in our lives, we build on each action.

What do you need to do to feel the best about yourself?

As women, we have to be unafraid of identifying our needs. And once we have identified these needs, we need to learn to actually fulfil them – without apology for wanting to do so.

What actions do you need to take to feel good about yourself on a day-to-day basis?

If you were to wake up every morning to an alarm that said, "Arise, you are loved!" you would feel internally nourished and ready for a great day. But if you were to wake up to an alarm that said, "Your thighs are fat!" how do you think your day is going to go? Probably better after the first doughnut, right?

It sounds so simple, I know, but what about instead of waiting to love ourselves before we take self-loving actions, we take self-loving actions that lead us to loving ourselves?

Small, consistent actions are a sustainable way of increasing our self-love. Doing things we love increases our self-love. Surrounding ourselves with beauty increases our self-love. And immersing ourselves in a pool of inspiration will skyrocket our self-love until we are giving ourselves so many self-love kisses, people will think we are insane.

Raw Beauty Actions

When we nourish our own beauty without using the latest anti-ageing skin cream, new diet or new bum-toning shoes to do it, we are in charge. No one can take away the beauty we create and nourish for ourselves, except us.

And because the Raw Beauty way is action-led, if we miss an action we can just take another one. No guilt, blame or sense of failure, we just take another action.

Personally, a small but powerful Raw Beauty Action I recommend is to stop buying trashy women's magazines that do not honour us or the women in them.

When my daughter turned one year old, I stopped buying these sorts of magazines because I did not want her seeing images that do not honour women and do not honour her.

Doing that consistently will make us feel better because if there is anything really important we need to know about who put on weight and who lost it last week, who has had botulism injected into their face or has shown their knickers while getting out of a car, someone will tell us.

Nourishment nugget
Stop dieting! Throw away your scales!

Setting boundaries

The powerful and rewarding journey of increasing self-love requires that we set boundaries for ourselves.

Firstly, we need to take the time to work out what nourishes us and who we are aspiring to be, and what raises us higher. We also need to work out what lessens us by leaving us feeling empty, lost and disempowered.

After we have figured that out, we need to set non-negotiable boundaries.

I told my partner in a relationship I was in many years ago, that for me to continue to be the person they had fallen in love with, there were two things I needed – time to look after my body and spirit, and to see my friends solo sometimes. This was non-negotiable for me.

Later, when I was first dating my now-husband and I was in England working as a chef and he was in Australia, I was struggling with the vast physical distance between us. He was on a nomadic spiritual journey so I would never know when he would get in touch, and I realised that I would be excitedly waiting around for days for him to call and then when we had spoken and I had put the phone down, I felt worse.

So I wrote him a very long email that was titled "I need..." and, you guessed it, listed extensively what I needed in a relationship and suggested that if he was not up for that, we should give it a miss.

Yes, it freaked him out, but he decided he was up for it.

CALIBRATING YOUR SELF-LOVE COMPASS

One of my current clients wants to be in a long-term relationship, and we were talking about different dating options because – as so many women forget – it is hard to find a relationship if you are not dating.

She had been chatting with a man online for a few weeks, and then it all went quiet at his end – he stopped communicating after they had both agreed to meet. She had then spent days trying to figure out what she had done wrong, and by the time we had our session together she was very upset with herself.

"It was going really well," she said. "I think I may have been too strong for him. I think with the next man, I will be less strong."

I asked her if she was saying, "The next time I date someone, I will be less me." And I asked her to remember that he was not choosing her, she was choosing him. She did not have to dumb down who she was or what she needed for him to choose her. She had a say in the matter. I asked her if she wanted to be with a man who could not cope with her strength. She ended the conversations with him.

When we can own who we are and what we need without apology or guilt, life becomes much easier. And when we are guided by our own self-love compass, it is ours to calibrate to our needs as time goes on.

Why so hard?

It seems the word 'yes' will fall out of most women's mouths every time they are asked to do something. Why is it so hard for many of us to set boundaries? Because it is part of societal conditioning – we are raised to be of service to others before we are of service to ourselves.

One of my clients, Joy, was told from a very young age that she was to put Jesus first, others second and herself last. This is an extraordinary woman who has had a lot of success in all areas of her life, but her conditioning has taught her to put everybody ahead of herself. So she found herself in her 60s exhausted from it all.

After some lessons in self-love, she is still a generous giver and continues to be of service to others, but now she has learnt to draw boundaries – she gives only when her own cup is full.

Filling our own cup

I talk a lot about having a full cup because we can only really give when our own cup is full – and self-loving actions are what fill it.

Taking time out to do something we love – even if the rest of the family hates it – is okay. Making a meal we love and they do not like is okay. We do not have to go around putting everyone's noses out of joint (although, to be honest, sometimes we do have to), but also we do not have to spend all our time trying to please everybody else, either.

When we are in cup-filling mode for ourselves and we have worked out how we are going to do it, we need to have conversations with others to help us plan the logistics. People are not always going to be happy with us, but it is essential to make cup-filling choices because how we feel about ourselves is paramount to how we are in our relationships.

The partners of many of my clients have supported them 100 per cent on their Raw Beauty Journey because they now have a happier, fulfilled person to share their life with.

Sharing by wow factor

One of the most beautiful miracles about the work I do with women is when family and friends take on the Raw Beauty Principles.

One client, Glenda, told me her husband and two teenage sons were so wowed by the woman she was becoming, they wanted in as well. Her sons had started looking after themselves better and were making Green Smoothies, and her husband declared that he, too, was a Raw Beauty Queen!

Another client, Jacinta, started taking her Green Smoothies to work and, before she knew it, she was running a very successful Green Smoothie Club. This involves 15 work colleagues all bringing in one or two pieces of fruit and some fresh greens every day, and using her Vitamix blender – which she generously took into work – to make different smoothie combinations for each other every morning.

This woman knew what she needed to nourish her body and this was her self-loving action; it was non-negotiable and she made it work, as well as sharing it with others.

When we can understand our own needs and communicate them in an inspiring and loving way, others may be inspired to take action in that area of their life, too.

Living your principles is so much more convincing than trying to persuade anyone of anything.

Live it, don't fix it

Do not waste your life 'fixing' yourself – spend your life living. Work to your strengths, not your weaknesses.

I think it is a mistake when we spend most of our time trying to improve all our many weaknesses when we could be having much more fun nourishing our strengths. It is probable that they became our strengths in the first place because we enjoyed doing them, so it makes sense to make them our focus – rather than what we struggle to do.

We all have limiting stories, thoughts and ideas about ourselves and what we can do. We say things like, "That's just not me", "That is not who I am", "I do not do that", "I cannot do that". But every time we say such things to ourselves and others, we limit ourselves and our expectations of ourselves.

We also grow older in mind, body and spirit when we refuse to step out of the box we have built around ourselves and our lives. My children's great-grandmother on my husband's side, Sasha Nekvapil, was an Olympic skier in her home of Czechoslovakia. She, her brother and husband escaped the fully armed communist army at night by skiing across an iced-over lake in petrified silence. Sasha only stopped downhill skiing at the age of 92, after she was injured when a snowboarder crashed into her.

What is a 92-year-old doing downhill skiing? Living!

Expand into yourself

As we expand what we think we are capable of and who we think we are, our lives get bigger – our self-love and self-worth increase – and life becomes a magical mystery ride of opportunities to expand and grow into continuously.

Statistics have revealed that women are less likely to go for jobs they do not feel 100 per cent qualified for, whereas men go ahead and work it out on the job.

Another example – the average woman spends 31 years of her life on a diet. Is that living? When it is possible to have a wonderfully rich and fulfilling life and not be a size four?

Our self-love and beauty come from the empowerment we allow ourselves through our regular actions.

Define your own success

One of the most powerful tools I have is 'my little success book'. At night before I go to bed, I open my little book and list three things that were a success for me on that day.

I do this partly because as an entrepreneur I do not have performance reviews, so I like to have a reminder of my achievements so I can celebrate them at certain times. But I also like to check in with myself that my day has largely represented the life I want to create for myself and my family.

This is such a nourishing practice. If you go to bed feeling a success, you wake up feeling a success. Well, unless you had some awful nightmare where you had to give a presentation and you looked down and saw you were naked apart from a pink tutu…

When I talk about my successes, I am not necessarily thinking just about earth-shattering, life-changing success – I am talking small day-to-day events, too.

Here's an example of an entry in my little success book:

October 30

1   I began an online touch-typing course. Very exciting.
2   Nice afternoon at home with the children.
3   In bed at 9.30pm!

While they are not exactly earth-shattering successes, they remind me that the life I am creating for myself is in motion. I am spending quality time with my children, I am honing my skills and I am looking after my body.

I feel successful.

We sometimes only feel successful when we have done the big things. But with big goals, we are usually so busy moving the goal posts we never actually get there. And meanwhile, even though we feel like we have been going nowhere, along the way we have missed acknowledging hundreds of smaller successes.

Do it in your words, your way

Learning to acknowledge the smaller achievements creates a foundation of self-love and self-worth that prepares the ground for the big stuff.

For my 40th birthday I decided to run a 45km marathon (I started running at 37 after I let go of one of my own 'I cannots'). If you have ever run a marathon, you will know there is a lot of attention on 'the numbers' – what is your PB (personal best time)? What was your longest training run? What is your goal speed per km?

This is how success is generally measured in the marathon world. But I had other goals to define my success – I did not want to get injured or sick during my training, as many runners do. I wanted to cross the finish line with my body intact and with a big smile on my face. I wanted to enjoy the journey and the spectacular views of one of Australia's most stunning coastlines. I wanted to meditate on my life from being a baby to where I am now, and be present to the life I have created.

I succeeded. And not only did I succeed, but there was unexpected magic along the way. Once I got to the 38km mark, I was listening to Pharrell Williams's 'Happy' to help me along and I found myself dancing! I could not feel my legs, but I was dancing.

Someone actually came up to me and asked if I was okay because people do not usually dance at the 38km mark...

Then, when I was about 200m from the finish line, my eight-year-old daughter ran out from the sidelines and held my hand, and we crossed the finish line together. The way she was smiling up at me as we ran together will be ingrained in my heart forever.

I then fell into my husband's arms and cried like a baby, and thanked the universe for my body and all it had done for me to this point in my life. And I thanked myself for believing that anything is possible if I want it enough.

What do you want? Define it for yourself and then create what success looks like to YOU. It is much more fun that way.

Get it out!

Don't just live your self-love, write about it. Writing down what is in our heads gets it out. Sometimes just the process of writing it down is enough. I very rarely read over what I write in my journal.

There is a reason people go on and on about journalling – it is because it works. In fact, here are four good reasons for writing in a journal:

- it allows us to be present to what is going on for us – good, bad or indifferent
- it gives us time with ourselves
- it can help resolve confusion and clear up issues, especially if we go back to what we have written and look at it with a different perspective
- our children can read it when we have passed away and realise how awesome we really were.

Do you have to write in your journal every day? Only if you want to – some people journal every day, others only write every couple of days or once a week. It is up to you. Whatever you decide, it is good to have journalling in your 'life tool box' in some way.

Breath

I had thought to title this section 'Meditation', but I hated the idea that you would either have a vision of sitting cross-legged in orange robes or skip this part because you have tried meditation before and it did not work, or because you do not have the time to meditate.

I hope that by the end of this section you will look at meditation in a new and empowering light. (You can, of course, wear orange robes if you want to.)

For me, meditation is about breath. Other people have different opinions, but that is my definition.

When we can slow down our breath, we slow our thoughts. When we slow our thoughts, we slow our mind. When our mind is still, we have the opportunity to be present to who we are, how we feel and what is running us.

On the Raw Beauty Queen Retreats, we do some form of meditation every morning. Doing this, I have discovered that the thought of slowing down is incredibly scary for some women. And after meditating, what many women discover is that when they are alone with themselves there can be deep sadness, resentment or anger. Also, they become aware of all the emotions they have not let themselves feel.

During a recent retreat, one participant became aware that she had not allowed herself time to grieve the death of her mother. Another said, "I cannot be inside my own head – it scares me."

The gift of sitting still and being with ourselves is possibly the biggest self-love action there is. When we can be with ourselves – with our thoughts, upsets, anger and disappointment – we can then begin to accept ourselves.

There is also a level of compassion that comes with this form of practice – compassion for our own life journey and the life journeys of others.

THE BREATH MEDITATION

If the idea of a simple breath meditation sounds like something you may want to try, read on.

Find a comfortable place to sit and close your eyes.

Inhale for the count of four.

1. 2. 3. 4.

Exhale for the count of four.

1. 2. 3. 4.

(How was that? Still here? Let's try it again.)

Inhale for the count of four.

1. 2. 3. 4.

Exhale for the count of four.

1. 2. 3. 4.

This is meditation. (And there was not even time to get into your orange robes...)

How many breaths like that do you think you have time for in your day?

Make it work for you

In my 20-plus years of yoga and meditation. I have changed the length of my practice according to my circumstances at the time. Before I had children. I would wake up at 4.30am every day and do yoga and meditation for two hours or more. Then when I was at home with young children, I would do my meditation practice in the shower every night – five rounds of the breath meditation you just did and I'd feel like a new woman.

Now my meditation practice is between 15 and 20 minutes a day, usually in the morning to set me up for the day. And if the morning gets away from me. I have been known to drop off my children at school and then do my practice in the car in the car park.

Have I ever missed a day? Lots and lots, actually. But now I am at a point in my practice where if I miss meditating for any more than two or three days, my mind starts to eat itself up.

When you plan your own meditation practice, remember that Raw Beauty is about small sustainable actions that you can do consistently. There is no point setting yourself up to fail, so make it achievable. I read in a book written by a very famous author that you must "just meditate for one hour in the morning and one hour in the evenings". I laughed.

Of course it is completely doable if you decide to dedicate your entire life to your meditation practice. But for me. I use meditation to 'hold' the life I am creating. I am not creating a life of meditation.

Letting go

My next insight into the self-love stakes is to let go of what no longer serves you.

Letting go sounds like it would be so easy, but in my experience it is actually one of the hardest things to do.

There are two kinds of letting go, and I think that they feed off each other. First there is the kind where you let go of negative thoughts and self-sabotaging behaviours and generally do a good search around your thought patterns and give them a thorough clean-out.

I used to find it so hard to even 'let' my friends go on holiday, I was so scared they would not come back. Sometimes I would sit in my room crying, preparing myself for someone else being lost from my life.

Depending on what the thoughts are and how long we have had them, they may never go away. But we can learn to manage them just by being aware of them.

The other form of letting go is to let go of the physical things that crowd our lives – letting go of clothes that no longer serve us, a couch that has done its time or old letters that you have no sentiment for.

Whether we are letting go of emotional or physical 'stuff', the over-riding feeling is one of lightness and space and new possibilities.

Some women have described it as a sense of freedom. All of this 'stuff' they have been carrying around, either physically or emotionally, has had a weight to it. And when we are brave enough to let these things go, it creates space not only emotionally, but in our lives as well.

I love the saying "You have to let go the good to make room for the great".

We do have to be willing to let go, though. If we want to create an improved relationship with ourselves, we must let go of what no longer serves us.

One of my clients, Anne, took an unconventional action in the name of letting go. She had a lounge suite and dining table and chairs, which she had owned for many years, that had some negative memories attached to them. As she was getting deeper into her Raw Beauty, she began to feel this furniture weighing her down in life and in some ways holding her back. So what did she do?

Yes, she did get rid of the furniture. But she went without replacement lounge and dining suites for some time. She was very clear about the old furniture having to go, and she was clear that she deserved nothing less than her dream furniture, so she went without until she could afford it and camped out in her bedroom until then.

All of her friends and work colleagues thought she was crazy to be doing this, but Anne was happy. She felt lighter, she felt free and she was enjoying her craziness.

For her, the fact that she was willing to be without what some would call a necessity was proof to her that she was shifting not only her furniture, but her thought patterns and her life in the direction she wanted to go.

She let go and she was free to create.

If we take this story and apply it to our lives, what do we put up with when we know or feel we deserve better? If we do not give ourselves permission to let go and take actions to increase our self-love, who will?

Celebrate yourself

"If the universe tried for a billion years, it would not be able to make an exact copy of you. Go dance or something!" – UNKNOWN

Most of us have one day a year when we have 100 per cent permission to celebrate ourselves – our birthday. Yet so many of us brush them off, like birthdays are a nuisance.

Why are we so scared of celebrating ourselves?

I love a birthday do. I love presents and I love being surrounded by my nearest and dearest. My birthday is not an annoyance to me. It is a gift.

So if you are one of those women who tries to find an excuse to avoid celebrating her birthday, look deeply and see if you can trace why.

A sense of unworthiness? Not wanting to be bothered? Not being good enough yet?

Of course there is the universal fear that no one will come to your party. But you do not even have to have a party – you can celebrate by yourself on the couch if you want, as long as you acknowledge and celebrate yourself nonetheless.

The other factor we miss out on when we avoid our birthday is the opportunity for others to celebrate us. Yes – people want to celebrate your life because it matters to them that you were born and that you have chosen to share your life journey with them.

You matter.

RAW BEAUTY JOURNEY
Inga, 24 years
Dancer and social entrepreneur

When I started work with Kemi and the 7 Principles of Raw Beauty, I felt ashamed of being beautiful and self-expressed. I felt guilty to prioritise self-care and self-love: to take time to do nothing and just be with myself.

What was missing from my life was the knowledge that who I am as a sister, daughter, friend, girlfriend and a woman is a field of possibilities for contribution, transformation and creation. I did not trust my gifts and was holding myself back in aspects of all my relationships. Though eating healthily, I did not have much empowerment around food and exercise.

The Self-Love Principle was powerful for me because I learnt that I am worthy – worthy of feeling loved, beautiful, vibrant and empowered. I understood that I deserve to put myself first and care and nourish myself in the same way I do for others. I learnt that I am the most important person in my life.

The biggest Raw Beauty Action I took on was creating a Raw Beauty Banquet for the women in my life. I tend to feel vulnerable expressing who I am, and in the past I would have kept it to myself rather than sharing. I had to step out of my comfort zone and express my gratitude and love for them, and thus expand myself in the area of self-expression. I also shared my new empowering actions in the area of food and exercise.

The biggest difference it has made to my life is how I now express myself and stand up for myself and what matters to me. I have learnt the importance of voicing what I need, and to ask for help. This is part of self-love. I also find it easier to give compliments and help other women love themselves. I still fall back into old habits, but this new awareness helps me realise when it happens.

Another example that illustrates this shift in me is that I pursued modelling work, which would have been unthinkable prior to the 7 Principles of Raw Beauty. I used to be ashamed of my physical beauty, but now that I own it I can be an example for other women.

I now see myself and my life as resourceful and abundant. I know that I am more than enough, in fact I feel that I am equipped to realise the loving and passionate life that I deserve. The most important lesson that I now practise daily is: when I honour and powerfully nourish myself, I experience an abundance of energy and a joyful desire to give to others. Now I feel far better equipped to support other women to know that they deserve to feel amazing.

Self-Love Questions

1 Do you need more self-nourishment?
2 When do you feel the most beautiful and proud of yourself?
3 What is the worst story you tell yourself about yourself? And is this story really true?

RAW BEAUTY ACTIONS

Which one can you add today?

1 Buy yourself a beautiful journal and start to release your thoughts, worries, fears and joys onto the pages. It is amazing the answers and insights we find when we put our thoughts on paper.
2 Begin a success journal today.
3 Set an alarm on your phone once or twice a day that says something elevating like, "I am becoming more beautiful every day" or "I am becoming kinder to myself".

So now you have begun to nourish your body, you have more energy and you have started to feel good about yourself, what happens next?

.

6

PRINCIPLE 3
Creative Expression

Nourishment nugget
Life creation is creativity at its best.

HONOUR AND NURTURE your creativity to express your whole self.

Soul nourishment

I grew up surrounded by creative people – creative in one way. My first two foster mothers were professional knitters and I spent many weekends at craft fairs with them both. It was wonderful to be around continual creation. What we can produce with our hearts, minds and hands is awe-inspiring.

But when I was not hanging out with crafters, I was made to believe that creativity was frivolous – not real, somehow. Either you did it if you were not smart enough to do anything else, or it was something you did for money if you could not do anything else. Finally, it was a hobby if you had the time.

I no longer think like that. I now know that nurturing our creativity is one of the most important things we can be doing.

Being creative is what nourishes our souls. When we are young children, it is all we do – we create continuously. And then somewhere along the line society says, "Enough of that! It is time to grow up."

And so we do, we 'grow up' and we wither.

A thing to be nurtured

Some of us were told we were no good at the thing we loved. One of my VIP coaching clients was working in the coal industry when we started working together and wanted to create her own health and wellbeing blog, as she wanted to share her incredible personal journey with others. Writing her first post came quite easily to her, but then she struggled with the second, third, and so on.

In our session, I asked how she was going. She was excited to tell me that it was not going well with the writing. Why excited? Because she had managed to trace back why she was struggling so much.

When she was a young girl at school, she had been given some homework that was to write a story. She spent a long time on her story and was very proud of it. After the teacher had marked the children's work (how you mark creativity I have no idea) the work was handed back.

As my client's work was handed back to her, the teacher said, "I hope you never want to become a writer!"

She did not write for more than 30 years.

We must never underestimate the power of the throwaway comment, to us or by us. But the wonderful thing is that she is now writing and, guess what? She is a fantastic writer.

Create as a priority

Everything that surrounds us was created by someone (except the universe, possibly – the jury is still out on that one) – every street sign, kitchen tile, book, toilet, song and set of stairs. Everything. It was created by someone using their creative talents and expression to provide something. Now, I am not suggesting you create a toilet, though you may want to, in which case I fully support you. But I am suggesting you put your creativity as a priority on your to-do list.

So many adults walk around with the idea they are not creative, but this way of thinking depends largely on what we decide creativity looks like. If we want to create works like a famous painter, then we may miss the mark. But if we are happy with putting colour onto a page, walking in a park or arranging some flowers in a vase, we can be creative.

Nourishing our creative expression is not about the end product at all but – as clichéd as it sounds – it is about the journey. It is about the fulfilment and joy we gain from our willingness to be vulnerable and have a go.

Create with kids

If we struggle to access the creative part ourselves, there is one way that will open anyone up to their creativity – hang out with children. But don't just watch them – be with them. You will bring a smile to almost any child's face if you ask them questions like "What would you like to make or build today?" or "What game shall we play or make up today?".

Of course you will need to be quick-witted, sharp and focused – the rules and boundaries for children's games can change in a heartbeat, depending on whether the child is winning or not. But roll with it – you are only in it to win the joy of creativity, and children can be our best teachers if we allow them to be.

Make time

How often we access our creative expression is up to us. If you love to sing, you can do that every day, but if you like to tango on mountaintops, you may not be able to do that as regularly.

The good news is, most of us have more than one way to express ourselves creatively. Me, I like playing with food, knitting, sewing, singing, gardening, interior design, galleries, writing letters, restoring furniture, painting, homemaking, reading books (you know, the old-style paper ones), and probably a heap more other things. Of course I cannot do all of them every day, but at least one gets a look-in most days.

We need to stop waiting for the time to do something creative. The time is never going to land in our laps. "Oh, here are three spare hours I forgot I had!" – that is never going to happen.

When my son was born, I still hung on to doing something for myself every day, other than having a shower. This was to knit at least one row of my knitting each night. I say "doing something for myself" ironically, because I was knitting a jumper for him.

Anyway, it was my time for me. And there was something about the fact I was creating something tangible that made the five minutes spent doing it feel like an hour.

It was my 'me' time – my meditation and my creativity all rolled into one. And when you have a newborn, even one row of knitting might be asking too much, but most nights I did it. Some nights I even knitted two rows!

Be flexible and have fun

Creativity does not have to be painting, sewing or knitting. One of my favourite ways to be creative is to make up stories for my children. I ask them to give me three things they want me to mention in a story – usually it is something like a bear, a girl and a Lego truck – and off I go.

This is so much fun. I always do something crazy – like getting the bear accidentally stuck to the Lego truck with the strongest honey in the land, and the Lego truck is going down a hill very fast. Then the girl saves the day by singing her heart out because she has the strongest voice in the land (yes, a very conscious plant for my children that a boy does not save the day and girls are strong), and this brings all of the magical birds from the forest to where the Lego truck is heading. The birds create a wall, as the girl has ordered them to do, and they stop the truck. They eat all of the honey together and the bear learns never ever to play with honey and Lego at the same time.

The end.

A masterpiece? Not really. Fun? Absolutely.

Nourishment nugget
Perfection is a party pooper – lock the doors on it!

Create for creation's sake

Are you a perfectionist? We probably all are in our own way. But when it comes to creative expression, perfectionism is not your friend. Not even a 'frenemy' (a friend and enemy in one). It is 100 per cent your enemy.

If you are a professional artist, then it may be good to have perfection as a frenemy – so you can be objective about your work and its commercial value. But, otherwise, perfection will spoil your creative party.

If we need for our creative endeavours to be perfect, we will never create. If we are concerned about other people's opinions of our creations, we will never create. We must learn to create for the sake of creating.

If you need help, here is a list of ways for you to get creative.

1   Spend time with creative people (children are always a winner)
2   Spend a day wandering in your favourite nature spot
3   Plant a garden
4   Play in a park
5   Build something – anything
6   Restore or mend something
7   Write a letter by hand to someone
8   Create a reading nook in your house
9   Read in your nook
10 Sit in places in your house that you would never think to sit
11 Write a bad song or poem, or both
12 Make up stories for your children, grandchildren, nieces and nephews, friends' children
13 Doodle

The possibilities are in fact endless – the key being you are being creative, not striving for perfection.

Now for the big stuff...

I have spoken about the tangible creations we need to indulge in to nourish our whole beings, but there is another form of creation – the ultimate creation. That is, the conscious creation of our lives.

Life creation is the most exciting and rewarding form of creation there is.

Me, I never used to know this was possible – I thought life just happened to us. Some people had bad stuff happen to them, some had good, and that was that.

I didn't grow up with anyone who seemed to be consciously creating their lives. Everyone was doing the best they could with what they had.

It was when I read my first personal development book in my late teens or early 20s that I was opened up to a way of living that I never knew existed. It allowed me to see that there was an energy to life, and that we had some say in how that energy was used.

It was a new world for me. And I have been creating my life ever since.

What are you creating?

RAW BEAUTY JOURNEY
Ros, 31 years
Corporate trainer

Growing up, I was a classic case of a teenager who hated herself. Why didn't I have straight hair like all the other girls? Why wasn't my hair blonde? Why were all the other girls skinnier... prettier... more popular? Life is so unfair! But most of all I always wanted to be older because, even under all the teenage angst, I had a feeling that age would change all this.

My early 20s came and went. University was no better than school. I was still the same old girl, known for the same old things – including being grumpy with 'a face' that could make adults cower. When I moved back to the family home after university, the years came and went with the same friends, the same hobbies... and my teenage self as evident as ever.

So, at the age of 27, I engineered a move to Australia with work, hopeful I could start again. I was eager none of the 'but that's not you' baggage that comes with old friends and family would travel from the UK with me.

Once there, my optimism was rewarded when I discovered the Raw Beauty Queen community. It was through exploring Kemi's 7 Principles of Raw Beauty at her raw food workshops and Raw Beauty Queen Retreat that I was given 'permission' to love myself. I discovered, by talking to others, that I was not alone, unique or strange. I learnt the amazing effect of nourishing, raw food – not a sudden 'rush' from drinking a Green Smoothie, but rather the gentle glow of knowing you are treating yourself kindly. I was challenged to say 'yes' to things I may previously have shied away from in order to live my passion. All through a community of women there to support not sneer.

So where am I now? Well, back in the UK for one, but now with all the empowerment of the Raw Beauty Queen community. But if you think this means I never have 'I hate myself' moments, then I'll have to burst your bubble. I do. However, they are rare now and when they do happen, I recognise them as 'just a thought', remind myself of why I'm so lucky, and that I do all I can to be the best version of me.

I now jump at chances to push myself – taking on a second job because it engaged me, then setting out to make my passion my living by studying a degree in Nutritional Therapy, on top of my full-time job. I enjoy nourishing my body with food that makes me glow, which means both drinking Green Smoothies and not turning down my mum's lovingly-made cake because it 'might make me fat'.

When I moved into a new flat, I set out to create a community by inviting everyone to a communal garden party.

I'm not 100 per cent raw, and I can't honestly say I make time for my creative interests, and I'm certainly not always the creator of joy. But when I lose my path I do have the 7 Principles of Raw Beauty to use to find my way and get back on track.

Creative Expression Questions

1 How do you want to create your life?
2 What is your form of creative expression?
3 Have you allowed creativity to be squeezed out of your life? What creativity would you like back or like to explore?

RAW BEAUTY ACTIONS

Which one can you add today?

1 Find 30 minutes a few times a week and get your creative groove on.
2 Today is a great day to start creating a vision board – a collection of images and words that create an inspired life map that puts creative expression and life creation together.
3 Write down three things you would like to create in your life.

———————————

So now you have nourished your body, you have started to feel good about yourself, and you are nourishing your creative expression and creating your life, what happens next?

7

PRINCIPLE 4
Joy Creation

Nourishment nugget
Joy is everywhere; if you choose to you can see it.

PRACTISE THE ART of gratitude. Joy comes from choosing joy, moment by moment. The idea of joy creation is not about having to be happy all of the time – it is about finding the joy and how to be grateful in most situations. I say most situations because sometimes terrible things just happen and there simply is no joy to be found. But our everyday circumstances surround us with opportunities to bring joy to ourselves and others.

Choose joy

In my late 20s I took part in a life-changing self-development course. It changed my life in many ways, but I would like to share this story to illustrate this particular principle.

As I talked about in Chapter 2, I had many primary carers growing up. And when I was in my early 20s, my birth mother married a wonderful man who made her extremely happy, and who is a great father and stepfather. But when it came to her asking me to call him Daddy (you always call your parents Mummy and Daddy in Nigeria, no matter your age), I refused and would only call him by his first name.

I was very clear that I had already had five fathers in my life and I was not going to have another one, thank you very much. And even though I knew my refusal and my 'I am right and stuff the lot of you' attitude wounded my mother and was disrespectful to my stepfather, I was not budging, not one inch.

During the course I was taking, however, I realised I was in the room with people whose fathers had walked out on them, died when they were young or were abusive, and all the other variables of an absent father. And I felt incredibly humbled and selfish.

It suddenly occurred to me that to have had five men welcome me into their hearts as their daughter for various periods of my life, even if only for a short time, was a priceless gift. And if one more wanted to open up his heart to me, meaning I was going to have six fathers, well bring it on!

I called my stepfather and thanked him for marrying my mother, for loving me and my six siblings, and for managing to successfully create a blended family of nine children. I told him I respected and loved him, and that from that moment onwards I would call him Daddy. His choked reply? "My daughter…"

From being right to being grateful, it was such a powerful lesson for me to learn. And I also learnt how giving joy – or choosing joy – creates joy, too.

Gratitude, joy, abundance and beauty

"I know about the bad things but I look only for the good things. Wherever you look, there is beauty everywhere," said Alice Herz-Sommer, the world's oldest Holocaust survivor, who died aged 110 in February 2014.

Like this woman, who you might think had good reason not to see the good in life, I like to think in terms of this equation: gratitude = joy = abundance = a beauty-filled life.

And the idea of abundance makes me smile.

You may not have an abundance of everything you desire, but the thought of abundance probably makes you feel good – it certainly does me. And it is possible to see abundance, have gratitude and create joy all at once, in one juicy hit. We only have to decide this is what we are going to look for and experience, and we will find it.

Think about being stuck in a traffic jam – a joyless circumstance in most people's minds, with not much gratitude to be found, and certainly no abundance other than the many cars packed bumper to bumper. But if you had inspiring audiobooks or your favourite music to listen to, there can be a shift in thinking. You can be grateful that you had the audiobooks in the car, and that you now have an abundance of time to listen to and gain joy from them.

Imagine you have your teenage son in the car with you. Normally pretty withdrawn and monosyllabic, he is suddenly held hostage in the car with you, and he speaks. Sitting in the immobile traffic, he shares what is happening for him and you feel a connection you have not felt in a while. He even smiles at you. So you feel grateful your son was with you, and that you had abundant time to listen, and the connection you are feeling brings you joy.

Here is another example. You do not get the promotion you wanted at work, but the support and empathy you receive from your co-workers (who you thought were cold and aloof) overwhelms you, and you are suddenly grateful for the caring work environment and the abundance of support, and this brings you joy.

Or maybe you miss the tram, but you have a very uplifting conversation with the other women who missed the tram.

A conscious switch in attitude or mindset is what is working here. In any situation we can ask, where is the joy in this moment? What can I be grateful for in this moment? Where is the abundance here?

If you do not ask these questions, the outer circumstances of your life – not you – will dictate your joy. Which leaves you like a feather in the wind, never knowing when joy may pass your way again.

If you can choose joy, abundance and gratitude as a habit, the world and the people in it become much nicer – magic and miracles can happen at any moment. Watch out.

Beware the joy police

Just one other thing about feeling joyous. When we do, some of us have an inner voice that says, "Erm, excuse me. You seem a little too joyous right now... things are a little too good to be true. It is probably time to pick a fight with someone – anyone – or get a cold, or put your back out again..."

Watch out for that inner anti-joy voice, and check in with yourself to see what you might be doing to decrease your own levels of joy. Sounds absurd that we would do that, does it not? But we do.

And just to let you know, I am not immune to this voice either. In fact, if you promise not to tell anyone, I will share what I do. When things are going exceptionally well for me, I think I am going to have a heart attack and die. Seriously.

It usually happens when I am in bed with my husband and I say, "Babe, I just want you to know that my heart is feeling a little funny. It has skipped a few beats today, I think."

And he replies, "Okay." But not with much interest, because he knows what is coming next.

"So," I continue, "if I have to go to the emergency department during the night, you have to tell the doctors your wife complained of heart problems at 10.53pm."

"Okay," he says, with a slight 'Here we go…' tone.

And, no, I have never had to go to the emergency department in the middle of night with heart problems and, yes, when all is good in our world he will jokingly say, "Things are pretty great right now, how is your heart?"

But it was great that I was able to share this with him. If we hold on to fears like this, we begin to believe them and then we are kind of stuffed when it comes to creating beautiful lives. After all, I would be managing my life around my impending heart attack.

What do you do to destroy your own joy? It may not be a heart attack drama, but you will have something. If we are aware of what we do, we can catch it, hear it and let it go. Or even have our partners make fun of us…

Attracting grateful and joyful people

When you are creating more joy around yourself and you are becoming more and more grateful, you attract people into your life who have the same nourishing habits of gratitude and joy creation. At the same time, you become very aware of the people around you who are constantly in a negative headspace and always complaining or gossiping. What to do?

Just keep being joyous and you may infect them.

Cultivating gratitude

When it comes to gratitude, we have an overflowing pot to harvest from – it is called our heart. Take a moment now and think of three things in your life you are grateful for. If you cannot find any gratitude, then saying this to yourself three times – "I am grateful that I am here" – is a good start.

One of the most powerful and nourishing tools I have ever used is writing a gratitude journal. I am sure you have heard of this type of journalling, and you may already do it. You can make it part of the daily journalling I talked about in Chapter 6, or have a separate Gratitude Journal.

If you are not already regularly writing down what you are grateful for, I highly recommend it as a way of looking at life through a different lens. This practice is not about forcing yourself to pretend you are grateful, like putting a mask over deep sadness, but about being genuinely grateful for your life and what happens in it.

You may decide that writing one line a day is enough to begin with – remember, small sustainable actions are key – or if you already love to write, you can write as many 'gratitudes' as you wish.

Start each entry with, 'Today I am grateful for…' or 'Right now I am grateful for…' and see how you go.

Sometimes I write 10 gratitudes a day, sometimes I write one, two or maybe three; how much we can write changes for many reasons. But the magic of gratitude writing is that the more gratitude you acknowledge, the more gratitude you experience.

Just because you can

I believe that bringing joy to others is one of the most joyous actions we can take – to decide we are going to enrich another person's life just because we can.

It feels wonderful to wake up in the morning with the question, "Who am I going to bring joy to today?"

No matter what challenges are going on in our own life, it is always possible to bring joy to others – even if we are not feeling it ourselves. And sometimes in doing so, we end up experiencing joy as well, as a positive side effect.

In my own life, I like to put notes in my children's lunch boxes telling them I love them. Even if they do not thank me or mention them, I know these messages brought my children joy when they saw them, and that is enough for me.

There are so many ways we can bring joy to others – I run a bath for my husband when he needs to wind down after a long week, and I love baking for my neighbours (and I love it when they bake for me). And if we are not sure what will bring joy, just ask. And then deliver it – not out of duty or guilt, but because you can.

The joy of things

I love things. There, I have said it.

I am not minimalist. But I am not a hoarder, either.

I used to find it really difficult letting go of physical objects because as a child I had so few things that were mine, and what was mine would often be lost with all the moving.

I do need to clarify what I mean by "I love things". I do not love just anything. I love beautiful things. For me, having a home filled with beautiful and meaningful things is very important for my heart and my head.

There is a saying in the design world – if it is not practical or beautiful, get rid of it. And I agree with that. I believe we need to release what no longer serves us and create space for something else – or maybe nothing else.

The words of an architect being quoted in one of my favourite interior design magazines still stick with me: "Your home should be filled with beautiful things – if they are useful that is great, but they must be beautiful first." I sort of love that it was not important to him if they had any practical use at all.

My idea of beautiful is not defined by what other people think. There are some very random objects in my home that others may not see as beautiful, but they are beauty to me. So whatever objects, pictures, music or even smells are beautiful and nourishing to you, surround yourself with them. If we make our homes a joyous place to be, they will nourish us and bring joy to all who enter.

Joyful surroundings

How would you feel if you were asked to sit in a room with three black walls and one dark grey wall, empty except for a broken chair in the middle? Or if you were asked to find a place to sit in a room full of random objects piled up around you – so many it felt suffocating and claustrophobic.

Never underestimate the effects of your home environment. Take time to create a sanctuary for yourself that makes you feel calm and happy.

About three times a year I set aside a day to have a brutal clean out, to deal with the inevitable build-up of 'stuff' in my home. I fill at least two big black bin bags – one with rubbish to throw out and the other with things I can pass on to a charity shop or on to friends.

I end up letting go of more than I thought I would, and afterwards I feel so clear and refreshed. And I have never regretted letting go of a single physical item.

Sometimes less is more.

Joy your way

I have walked into homes where I have felt I could not sit anywhere for fear of ruining the perfect set-up. It can be too much. So rather than following all of the latest trends and ending up with homes that are carbon copies of each other, we can be inspired by design gurus but put our own spin on it.

Surround yourself with your version of joy.

RAW BEAUTY JOURNEY
Glenda, 54 years
Home and farm manager

This year for Mother's Day, my son began his card with these words: "To my dear Mum, who seems to get healthier and more vibrant each day…"

This was a beautiful affirmation of how my life has changed so positively in the past year through following Kemi's 7 Principles of Raw Beauty.

When I started on the Raw Beauty Journey, I was absolutely depleted after 20 years of struggle with chronic fatigue, and the depression that comes with feeling so exhausted and inadequate for so long. I was caught in the downward spiral of being too busy and too tired to care for myself effectively, while needing to and wanting to care for others as well. Life felt like a struggle most days.

My world changed dramatically the moment I was prepared to let go of the struggle and commit to a new journey with the Raw Beauty Principles. And it has been a truly beautiful journey.

It started with me accepting the importance of nourishing myself and making this a priority. I added daily smoothies and more raw and whole foods, and my energy levels lifted within days. With more energy I could exercise with a sense of joy and pleasure, rather than seeing it as another 'should' in my day. I found myself smiling once more.

If these new nourishing habits had been the end of the journey for me, I would have been perfectly thrilled, but the magic was just beginning and continues to build in my life each day.

I began to value myself more and be more compassionate with myself. I was able to let go of the power I gave to negative voices and stories in my head and create new, exciting stories. I reconnected with the incredible power of creativity, joy and passion, and learnt practical tools to expand these areas on a daily basis. The nourishment and joy expanded even further.

Kemi's teachings and wise, practical ways of challenging past patterns and replacing them with new nourishing patterns have given me the gift of choice and power in my life. This has been the most wonderful part of the journey for me and has strengthened my confidence, calmness and courage to move further along this path.

I no longer feel powerless. The struggle has gone and I can now greet each day with gratitude and intrigue. I am healthier, happier and living with more passion than ever before.

On those messy, wobbly days when life throws curve balls at me, I know I have the tools to observe what's happening and make confident choices. I have been given a sustainable practice for the years ahead – not just a short-term lift.

This journey takes commitment but we are worth it and it is one joyous ride!

I am thrilled Kemi's teachings will reach many more people through this book, and know many will be blessed if they choose to nourish themselves in this way.

More nourished people and a more nourished world really excites me. Thank you, Kemi.

Joy Creation Questions

1   Are you a joyous person?

2   Where do you gain most of your joy?

3   Where is joy lacking most in your life?

RAW BEAUTY ACTIONS

Which one can you add today?

1   Choose someone in your life to whom you can bring joy and write a letter expressing your love; it does not have to be elaborate, and it does not need to be a romantic love letter – I have written such letters expressing my love to friends, parents, teachers and work colleagues. You can start the letter with, "I think you are beautiful/ wonderful because…"

2   Go around your house and collect three items that are not beautiful to you and donate them to a charity shop – someone else will find them beautiful.

3   Ask someone in your life what would give them joy right now, and do it for them if you can.

So now you are nourishing your body and you are starting to feel good about yourself, and you are nourishing your creative expression and creating your life, and life is becoming more joyous, what happens next?

8

PRINCIPLE 5
Elevating Relationships & Communities

Nourishment nugget
As we elevate others, we elevate ourselves.

SURROUND YOURSELF WITH people who support and nurture you to create a life you want to live. Build a community of women that will raise you higher and be this person for others.

Under the influence

Most of us would like to think we are our own person – an individual who only does what we want to do. That no one has a bigger impact on what we do than us. And in some ways this could be true – if we were 100 per cent grounded in who we are, our values and what we stand for. But, otherwise, I would say poppycock!

We must never be fooled into thinking the people we spend our time with do not have a huge impact on our lives. They can influence who we have a relationship with, where we work, what we eat, how we talk, what we wear, what we read, where we live and so much more.

Why did I stay being an actor for so long? Because everyone around me wanted me to stick at it, and I did not want to let them down.

I can pick up my children from school and they can give me a long list of the things they want to do when they get home. They are very sure of what activities they are going to fill the afternoon with – until one of their friends comes around to see if they want to play. My children may even say, "No, I do not want to play today." But usually all it takes is one "Oh, come on…" and one of them is off out the door with the friend. And as soon as one of them is off, the other one goes, too.

How many times have you said to yourself, "I am only having two glasses of wine tonight" and then someone says, "Go on, have another one" and you have a third.

Motivational speaker Jim Rohn beautifully summed up the need to think about who is influencing you:

"You must constantly ask yourself these questions: Who am I around? What are they doing to me? What have they got me reading? What have they got me saying? Where do they have me going? What do they have me thinking? And most important, what do they have me becoming? Then ask yourself the big question: Is that okay? You are the average of the five people you spend the most time with."

The female trust factor

There is nothing like knowing you have a group of female friends to 'hold' you in life – the ones you can be completely vulnerable with, who push you forward and believe in you when you don't and, if you are lucky, make really good food or know the best restaurants.

Women are so powerful when we come together to support each other and raise each other higher. But when we pull each other apart, that's another matter.

Many women do not trust other women. In fact, on my Raw Beauty Retreats, at least one third of the women struggle to trust other women, and we spend a fair amount of time looking at this.

One of my oldest and dearest friends used to be a model. She is stunningly beautiful, intelligent, generous, hilarious and worldly. She is an awesome woman.

When we used to be out and about together in London or New York, I would catch other women looking her up and down. They would often roll their eyes in a particular way, and I could see they had decided she was a bitch.

How often this happens concerns and alarms me. As women, if we cannot appreciate the internal or external beauty of one another, we are wildly off track in creating anything like the elevated community I dream of being a part of. Women have to stop hurting and competing against each other.

Can we please sort this out now!

A history of criticism and betrayal

One of the things that comes to light on the Raw Beauty Retreats is the effect on the participants of their past experiences with other women. They may have been betrayed by another woman in some way, or they may have been so preoccupied with what other women think of them that they have shut off communication and connection. One woman even became a truck driver so she would not have to be around or close to other women on a daily basis.

That may sound extreme, but we all have coping mechanisms to avoid repeat pain and disappointment.

Some of my harshest critics have been women. The people I have been betrayed by the most have been women.

THE EVIL GOSSIP GAME

When I was working as a chef and had just returned from my yoga teacher training in India, I decided to practise Ahimsa, which means no injury to living beings with your thoughts, words and actions.

As part of this, I decided I would not start or listen to any gossip about another person for one week. But I did not tell any of my work colleagues I was doing this, and I would remove myself from conversations or try to subtly change the subject.

That was a very lonely and quiet week for me! It was like I was on my own self-imposed silent retreat.

I realised that most of the conversations that went on were gossip – but I hardly deserved a halo because just a week earlier I had been very much a part of that gossip. Following that gossip-free week I realised that I felt better about myself because I was not putting someone else down for my or other people's enjoyment. I had developed more personal integrity by not getting involved, and it sat well with me, and still does.

Of course I am only human and I do sometimes get hooked, but it does not take long for me to become aware, check myself and stop.

It is particularly challenging for me, however, when I find myself in a gossip session in full swing. But when I do, I try to change the subject gracefully or remove myself, or I will be straight and say, "I understand you are very angry/passionate/upset about X, but I do not feel comfortable being part of this conversation because I would not like those things said about me."

TIME TO TAKE STOCK

How much do you gossip? How do you feel when you do? How do you feel when you are being gossiped about?

If you are in a group of women and they are gossiping about a woman who is absent from the group, there is a good chance they will be gossiping about you when you are not present.

There is a saying about this I really like: "What Susan says about Jane says more about Susan than it does about Jane."

Creating a like-minded collective

When we do give out a particular energy – and I see this all the time – we will attract into our lives people who are walking the same path as we are. And when these people are elevating, joyous, creative and generous in their words and actions, it will have a major positive impact on our lives.

Our intention needs to be to create a group of female friends that can celebrate each other's achievements with pure generosity of heart – no judgement, envy or competition.

We should never underestimate the power of women coming together. Throughout history awful things have happened to women to keep us disempowered, and many practices still exist today – some of them cleverly less overt to guarantee their survival.

There is no time like the present for women to come together in full force in support of each other, and there is so much for us to do on and for the planet right now. But if we spend that time pulling each other apart, we will not experience how extraordinary we are and we will never see what is possible for us as a collective or as individuals.

The benefits of belonging

I feel incredibly blessed to be a female entrepreneur working in the wellbeing space. It is an industry that leans heavily in the direction of women (we love to heal others as we heal ourselves) and the community is so incredibly generous. We do not come from a place of scarcity and lack. We all contribute to each other in the best ways we can and the win/wins are magical.

There is nothing like being part of a generous and open community. When we want to shift anything in our lives, the people around us have a huge impact on our success.

Just think of times when we have wanted to achieve something but the people around us have not been supportive, either because of fear for our wellbeing or due to feeling threatened by our desire to change.

I have never been a big drinker – give me one or two glasses of wine and I am pretty tiddly. But in the past when I have gone out for an evening and not wanted to drink, the pressure to do so was quite strong.

"Oh, just have a little one." "Don't be a bad sport." "You are so boring!"

Not exactly the kind of support we would expect from friends.

Take a moment to think of a time when you really wanted to achieve something but did not. Did you have a supportive group of women around you?

In days gone by, I would often give in and have a drink if pressure was applied. But not anymore. Not now the community that I am part of respects my decision. Again I say, never underestimate the power of a firm foundation of support, encouragement and non-judgement in the pursuit of our own life creation.

We need to take the actions that matter, and no one else can do that for us. But we will achieve more and create more when we have nourishing relationships to support us on the journey. We want to be with women who, when you say something like, "I was thinking of running naked through the streets, wearing a hat shaped like a banana!" will respond by saying, "Fantastic, why didn't we think of that? Can we do it with you?"

You do not want someone who will say, "You will get cold."

When we share our dreams with others, we are at our most vulnerable and sometimes our most suggestive.

SUPPORTED CHANGE IS GOOD

How many times have we shared something very close to our heart and were ridiculed, shot down or even shamed? And what did we do next? Many would either stop sharing the big things or completely close off the dreaming part of their life. But as we start to surround ourselves with nourishing relationships and communities, we will get positive responses no matter what, and other people in our life will notice and may not be happy about it, and may even be threatened.

A classic version of this is being told, "You've changed!" – but as more of an accusation than an observation.

Perfect. That is exactly the sort of comment we want to hear. If we are not changing, growing and expanding, somewhere along the line we died. We are living beings and that is what we are meant to do. We are meant to change, evolve, grow and expand.

"You've changed!" can actually be someone's way of saying, "You are not fitting into the box I created for you that worked for me."

Also, when people react negatively to our life changing, it can be because it has made them look at their lives and not be happy with what they see. However, this has nothing to do with us, and is no excuse for not creating the life we want.

Dealing with the dream stealers, negative whiners and gossipers

We know who these people are in our lives, but what do we do when we are in conversation with them? Do we placate them? Agree with them? Give only a little of ourselves because we know they will have a negative comment about whatever we say...

Most of the women who do this may be worried or concerned and have our best interests at heart. We may have done exactly this quite innocently in the past. But, to be honest, some of these women are plain destructive.

When we leave a conversation with women like this who are dream stealers, negative whiners and gossipers, we feel awful, burdened and joyless. Not only about ourselves but sometimes about life in general. They get under our skin and tarnish everything that feels like gold to us. They are not in any way interested in our being the best version of ourselves or living a life that nourishes and fulfils us.

Thankfully, having fewer of these women in our lives is not a matter of doing anything unkind or drastic, like giving them the chop or making a voodoo doll and sticking pins into it. What I have done over the years is to increase the number of elevating and supportive women in my life.

In energy terms, what tends to happen is as you spend more time with the supportive women, the destructive women tend to fall away.

This happens for a few reasons. One, when we start to respond differently to these women, the dynamic will naturally change and they may dump us! Or, as we are elevating ourselves, their negativity will be increasing and we will find we are spending less and less time in their company, and over time the relationship will lose momentum.

In my experience, having these destructive women in my life has always been an opportunity to look within myself and ask, "Why do I have a friendship with this person? What is in it for me?" Because there is a payoff for everything we do.

An opportunity to look within

Sometimes it may be difficult to work out what the payoff is – what could we possibly want from someone who treats us badly? But usually the payoff is something like we get to go to nice places with them, they have connections we do not have or they give us kudos when our identity is linked to theirs.

This is really important for us to look at. Whatever we discover about ourselves does not make us a bad person – our power comes from being able to admit to these aspects of ourselves and then shift them.

Being authentic

A good test for discovering whether a relationship or community is right for us is whether we feel, respond and behave authentically in it. Or do we pretend, hold back or silently cringe within a relationship or group.

For example, something really exciting is going on in our lives but we have not told certain people because we do not want to upset them, or we are worried they will think we are showing off.

I was plagued with this for a long time. I would censor the good things that were happening for me because I was afraid my friends would judge me.

My husband and I were planning a seven-week tour around Europe with our children. It was going to be our big adventure, and we were visiting Sweden, Switzerland, Paris, England, Barcelona, and ending in Thailand. To say we were excited is an understatement.

Standing in the school playground, I was asked by another mother what we were doing in the school holidays. So I told her, and got this response – "Well it is alright for some…" – with a slight sting in the tail.

In the past this would have made me feel sick to the stomach, and I would have gone into justification overdrive – "Well, we have to go because my family are there and my husband's sister is there, and it is actually really cold in Europe at this time of year and it gets really dark early, and I might fall over, and it can be so crowded in London and…" Justify, justify, justify…

But what I did this time was take a deep breath and simply say, "I feel incredibly blessed and very excited."

And it felt good. It felt good to own the life that I create with my family.

You are allowed to shine

Do you ever find yourself dumbing down your joys or achievements? In my birthplace of England, one does not talk too much about one's achievements or joys. And in Australia this is known as tall poppy syndrome – if you get too big for your boots, you will be brought back down to size quickly. (It is one reason why I love the American culture, where you can share what is going on for you and you are celebrated and encouraged.) So in a culture where this is frowned upon, we can easily find ourselves having to censor the good bits about our lives that we are proud of or excited about.

However, I have an extraordinary group of girlfriends who are all playing big in their lives, and it is a joy to be able to share all of the magic that occurs for each of us. What I found is that when we authentically share our lives, the good and the bad, it gives others the permission to do the same.

You know how it is. You are at a gathering and someone begins to talk about the weather and that is where the level of conversation stays. But if someone goes straight into authentically sharing that they are going through a divorce, the conversation becomes authentic very quickly.

The same goes with the tone of conversations. If one person starts whining about life, that is where it stays. It reminds me of one of my favourite Monty Python sketches, where the usual characters are arguing about who had the worst childhood. I think it ends when one of them says, "You lived in shoe box? You lucky bastard, I lived in a matchbox!"

Why do we find it so hard to celebrate ourselves and each other? I am not talking about showing off, which is completely different. We know the difference between arrogance or showing off and someone who is genuinely sharing about their life's joys and successes.

Even now I sometimes struggle with sharing all of the good bits. Just the other day I purposely left out a great thing that was happening for me because I thought I would be judged. But I am working on it because I do not want my daughter to dumb herself down for anyone. I have lived there and it hurts.

For the record, though, if you knew my daughter you would see no sign of this particular issue affecting her right now. But I worry about when 'life' gets to her. I want both my children to be proud of who they are and what they create in their lives for themselves and others.

Tap into the success of others

What I do make sure that I do is to support women to live big and fulfilled lives. I want to hear about all the wins – I want every detail. I think sometimes I am more excited than the people actually living the success. I am inspired by other people's successes because it shows me what is possible.

How do you react when another person shares their joys with you? Are you proud and inspired or do you find yourself judging them or being envious, resentful or negative?

Sometimes when someone else shares their good stuff, to us it is a reflection on what is not working in our lives. But we can use this as an opportunity to make the shifts we need to make for ourselves.

The clever thing to do is to ask the successful woman how she does it. Because if she has done it, there is no one better to learn from, is there?

Finding a new tribe

So, where are these great women who will not gossip about us, and with whom we will feel safe enough to be authentic around? Well, you know the saying, like attracts like.

We have to become nourishing and supportive women ourselves to attract similar women into our lives. We have to be the change we want to see in our world. Annoying, isn't it, that we have to work on ourselves to get what we want?

But another way to attract elevating, supportive and nourishing friends is to move out of your comfort zone – because Raw Beauty is about life creation and fulfilment, so taking focused action will yield better results than any wishy-washy I-will-see-how-it-goes approach.

Go on, try out the age-old anxiety- and vulnerability-fuelled question you may not have asked anyone since you were five years old – "Excuse me, will you be my friend?"

Yes, crazy, I know – but it works. I have found some of my closest and most elevating friends from being vulnerable enough to ask this question. And if you need help with the script, it could go also something like this:

"I think you are awesome. I too am awesome. Let's be friends!" Voilà! Done.

If you ask, you may get a yes – or a no. But either way you will have expanded yourself and got out of your comfort zone. If you do not ask, however, you get nothing.

Being a good friend

As a foster child with a succession of six sets of primary carers while I was growing up, I did not feel I could count on who my next family would be. Because of this, I put a lot of time and energy into my friendships, and I still do.

I am in no way a saint – I miss birthdays, I can be insensitive, and I have made flippant comments that have wounded a friendship for a period of time. But once I am committed in my friendships, I am loyal, reliable and willing to do whatever it takes to nourish that relationship. I love writing letters and cards and sending out care packs of my favourite goodies as surprises. I love giving gifts, and I love the thought of my friends' faces when they open the card or box.

I will look after your children. I will make you food for the first six weeks after you have given birth. I will give you a kick up the bum when needed, but I will also support you. I will say what others are afraid to say. I will not gossip about you. I will clean your house and I will hold you for hours when snot and tears are streaming down your face. I will believe for you when you have nothing left. I want you to live the best life you can.

Do not ask me to look after your pets. I am not the friend to ask to look after your pets! And did I mention, I will not remember your birthday.

What sort of friend are you?

What sort of friend do you want to be?

How we nourish our friendships and treat our friends is how we nourish and treat ourselves.

RAW BEAUTY JOURNEY
Susan, 53 years
Creative dance educator

At the age of 53 years, experiencing changes in my body, running a business, being a mother and a wife and rushing about with daily life, I was becoming exhausted and beginning to resent all I cared for. I felt I had to do it all. I felt overwhelmed.

A friend told me about Kemi's seven-day Raw Beauty Retreat, so I read about the 7 Principles and for the first time in my life decided to do something purely for me. It took courage and a certain blind bravado to take the first step.

The first principle – Body Nourishment – interested me, as I felt this would support my health issues, weight gain and feelings of lethargy. This was the principle I decided to work on. Upon commencing the retreat, I realised the rest of the principles – self-love, creative expression, joy, passion, relationships and purpose – were areas I needed action in as well.

Throughout my time away, I learned so much about myself. I had challenges and moments of clarity. I laughed, cried, hugged, talked and bonded with a group of women who were, and still are, nurturing, giving and supportive while on this incredible journey – my life.

Since returning home, my attitude towards life has changed. It is now more to do with how I am in it.

This, for me, is a huge shift. It is life-changing. I have energy and passion; I wake up in the morning grateful for each day; I smile. It is as if the huge, heavy cloud I have been struggling with has evaporated. I enjoy who I am and what I achieve throughout each day. I have put in place daily practices to support this. However, and I believe it is important to be honest in this testimonial, as well as having a wonderful life, husband, family, friends and work, all for which I feel blessed, things can, and indeed do, go awry. At the moment I am dealing with personal family issues that have been thrown at me. Kemi has said, "Sometimes people will throw plates at you." Well, these are platters!

I know we all have moments in our lives when things that are hard are thrown our way and, to be truthful, in the past I would have felt overwhelmed, stressed, guilty, blamed myself and let the ensuing thoughts take control. Those tendencies are still there. I feel them urging me to fall back to my old ways of coping.

However, since doing the Raw Beauty Retreat and taking on the 7 Principles, and having worked on building the skills to sustain myself, I find that I am dealing with what comes my way differently. I experience calmness and equanimity; I am more sure of who I am, stronger in my beliefs and not so much at the mercy of my emotions. This has been, and continues to be, reinforced by me committing to six months of coaching with Kemi. Plus, the coaching has enabled me to embark on some important personal goals that I would not have envisaged me being capable of doing.

I feel an incredible sense of wellbeing and no matter what outcomes may occur, I am in control of me, and I am getting the best from myself. I have a new-found sense of integrity, and I cannot state this more powerfully: this is truly liberating.

I believe in my abilities, and I accept what comes my way. Thank you, Kemi, for this gift.

Elevating Relationships & Communities Questions

1   Who are the five people you spend most of your time with?
2   Do you need to make some choices about the influences you allow into your life?
3   Who do you want to be for others?

RAW BEAUTY ACTIONS

Which one can you add today?

1   Try not to be involved in any gossip today. See how you go.
2   Tell another woman three things that make her a beautiful friend for you.
3   Ask someone today what is exciting for them in their life right now, and listen.

———————

So now you are nourishing your body and starting to feel good about yourself, nourishing your creative expression and creating your life, and life is becoming more joyous. You are attracting people into your life who raise you higher, and creating a safe environment for you to be yourself, so what happens next?

9

PRINCIPLE 6
Living Your Passions

Nourishment nugget
Passion is life's fire – ignite yours.

BE A FULL *expression of your passions and therefore a full expression of yourself.*

This is probably the scariest of all the principles because it takes extreme guts to live our passion, and I truly believe that when we are a full expression of our passions, we are a full expression of ourselves.

Why is it so important?

- Passion makes life easier
- Where passion lives, flow lives
- Passion makes life exciting
- Passion makes you constantly expand and grow
- Passion inspires others
- Passion gives life meaning

Passion is being alive

While it would be so much easier to live a safe life – keep our heads down, follow the status quo and not put anyone's nose out of joint – acting on our passions delivers so much more.

We all had many passions as children. When someone asked us what we wanted to be when we grew up, we used to list lots of things that probably had no link other than that we were passionate about them.

On the street where I live we are very blessed to have neighbours who are also our friends and allies, and it is not by accident – we all wanted our children to experience living in community, which means that most days after school, one of three neighbouring houses has a decent group of children eating their food and messing up their lounge room.

The other day one of my neighbour's sons volunteered this information: "Do you know what I want to be when I grow up? My response, " A camel?" "Nooooo," he said. "When I grow up, I want to be a scientist, an actor and a pilot."

This was said matter of fact. I told him that it was great he loved so many things. He smiled and went back to the Lego.

There was no way I was going to reason with him. He is a passionate child and it is not my place to make him be 'rational' or 'realistic'. I believe it is my role to elevate and validate him, and I hope he works out how to act in a cockpit while conducting world-changing scientific experiments. But there is a strong chance, as the years pass, many well-meaning adults will share their 'wisdom' and advise him that he should choose to be just one thing. Or he will pick up from the reactions around him that to many his dream is stupid, and he will dumb it down.

Did you have your passions dulled as a child?

Why so scary?

Continuing to acknowledge and live our passions is scary – it takes us out of our comfort zone, people may not support us, and some may even try to stop us. As adults we even try to stop ourselves when we say we are too old, that our idea is stupid and we will fail, that we have no time for it and that there are more important things to do.

The reality is that when we go after our passions, sometimes we will feel alone, sometimes it will be really hard work, and sometimes we will fail, look stupid and most likely weep. In fact, I promise you there will be weeping – maybe even snotty sobbing – and some of the tears will be from extreme joy while some will be due to deep pain and disappointment.

But once we are in the throes of living a passionate life, we would not give it up for anything.

Fear of the unknown

Where passion is, miracles are waiting for us. Passion lifts us to another level. But living our passion sometimes goes against everything we were raised to do – to settle down, find a good job and be secure. And that is why when we share our passions with others, sometimes their social conditioning and personal fears react with our ideas or plans.

Some people will not understand – in fact, most people will not understand – and this is why elevated communities and relationships are so important. And you need to understand that fear of the unknown is what stops many people from living a passion-filled life.

We are taught the 'better the devil you know than the devil you don't' rule from an early age, and we focus on what would be the worst that could happen, instead of focusing on the best that could happen.

Get out of your comfort zone

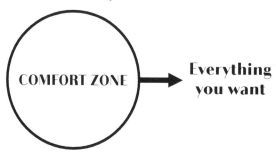

In my own life I had been a successful actor for seven years, I had worked with two of England's top theatre companies, worked in TV for three years and managed to squeeze in a Hollywood movie – do not get too excited, I said one line – but then I started to think that maybe I did not want to be an actor any more.

Even though this thought would keep popping up, I didn't listen and kept pushing it aside, thinking how great my life was, how I was getting good money and how I could be doing worse things. And there was a part of me that felt I had to keep doing it because other people would kill to have my life, as I was repeatedly told.

But one night, after coming off stage in New York, I was wiping off my make-up when I had the thought that I did not want to do this. It was fun, but it is not why I was here. I was surrounded by people for whom acting was an absolute passion – who had wanted this since childhood. But it was not my passion.

My real passion

At that time, my real passion was food. But it took me another 18 months to leave acting because I allowed everybody else's thoughts, feelings and opinions to be more important than mine.

I eventually got to a point where I felt like I was selling myself out, however, that I was not being true to myself. Then I got really courageous.

During a conversation with a close friend, Gisella, I had told her that I wanted to travel the world as a yoga-teaching chef (there was not a class on this particular career at school). So a week later she had set me up to have a meeting with a man who needed a chef for his resort in Thailand.

The job brief was that I needed to teach the Thai chefs how to cook European food to a high standard. There was no pay, but accommodation and food were paid for.

Meanwhile, my agent had been negotiating a dream deal with a major television company in the UK, which was taking weeks and weeks.

When I got home from my meeting with the resort owner, there was a message on my answer phone from my agent saying that the TV deal had come through, it was an amazing contract and that I should go on holiday because I started filming in a week.

I knew in that moment that this was it – this decision was going to be one of the biggest I would ever make in my life. I could go to Thailand for no pay with a man (and his wife) who I had met only once in a pub, or take on one of the best TV contracts ever offered to a black actress at that time.

I could literally see the crossroads in front of me and my head was spinning. How would I pay my mortgage? What would people think of me? Was I being ridiculous? Was I being ungrateful? Who is this man? What if the resort does not exist? What if they just want to murder me?

I inhaled and I exhaled, and… I decided to go to Thailand. And not only that, I decided to register on a yoga teacher training course in India.

Saying yes with no regrets

Even though many of the reactions to my decision from family and friends were extremely upsetting, I knew that I had to do this. I was being pulled into it and I did not want to resist. And as I explained in Chapter 2, Thailand was life-changing for me.

I was doing what I had declared to my friend I wanted to do – I had travelled, I was chefing and I was about to learn how to teach yoga in the country where it had originated. I would spend my days doing hours of yoga, preparing meals for the guests wearing my swimming costume (health and safety were not invited to this party) and I learnt how to authentically cook one of my all-time favourite cuisines (I make a mean Pad Thai).

But the best outcome of saying YES to myself for myself was that I discovered dreams could come true. And an extremely unknown outcome was that I met my future husband in Thailand.

Do I regret leaving acting? No, not at all.

Sometimes I will see a play or a movie and I think, wow, they would have had such fun filming that or, wow, that would have been an amazing role to study, but I do not have any regrets.

What it takes

What does it take to start living our passions? It takes being willing to step out of our comfort zone – to be willing to be really scared and unsure. It takes trusting in ourselves when maybe those around us do not. It takes commitment, focus and being comfortable with being uncomfortable. It takes being vulnerable. It takes action.

We were put on this planet to be no other than our individual selves. We might be told otherwise, but we experience the greatest joy, connectedness and fulfilment when we are doing what we love to do.

Make a declaration

So how do we start this passionate living? It depends where we are in life and what we want going forward.

I know that one of the most powerful actions we can take is to share our passion with at least two people who love and respect us. Once we are not the only ones holding it, it creates a circle of support. Once we have made the declaration about what we intend to do, the wheels are set in motion for something to start happening. Just like my declaration to Gisella.

Start positive actions

Our first steps may be taking a class in the chosen area or taking a leap of faith and applying for other jobs. Another action is to volunteer where our interests are – and not just for charitable organisations. We can volunteer to do anything if we are brave enough. And most businesses love people who are passionate and are happy to work for free!

Getting up and doing it is the best start. If our passion is hiking, we do not spend years reading about how to do a hike, we just go and do one, and learn along the way. If our passion is to sing, take lessons, go to an open mike night or decide that every week you will write a new song. If you want to rule the world because you know you could do a better job than is currently being done, start with making a difference to those around you.

However we decide to do it, it is always possible to live our passions every day.

Getting REAL

You may not feel that you can take a leap of faith like I did and completely switch careers. Maybe you think your job gives you a good enough salary and enough fulfilment, or maybe it funds your passion for space travel. Maybe you have been too scared to dig deep enough within yourself to discover your passion. Or maybe you were told by someone else (or yourself) a long time ago that your dream was silly and you needed to get real.

For me, REAL stands for Realising Every Action Lives. That is, every action we take either takes us further towards the life we want for ourselves, or further away.

It is up to us.

Lose limiting beliefs

This is a huge topic and there have been many, many books written on the subject because we are all consumed with limiting beliefs – it is part of the human experience. Even the most successful people in the world have limiting beliefs, but they learn to find out what those beliefs are, explore them and then create tools to manage them.

A few years back I was told that I should not run. I have had two wonderful homebirths but after my daughter was born, my hip was misaligned and would get sore, and a personal trainer – who was someone I respected very much – told me that the grinding action on my hips when I was running would not be good for me. And I believed him.

Also, back in my late teens, I decided to go running with my Dr. Martens boots on (I think I may have had a hangover) and did some damage to my knee.

So, with the opinion from the personal trainer and the minor damage I had done to my knee, I believed that I could not run. I loved it, but I could not do it. And for three or more years I went around saying, "I would love to run but a professional told me I can't." And everyone would say, "Oh, okay." They believed it because I believed it.

However, after several years of eating raw foods and healing and nourishing my body, I wanted to run. I actually felt like I needed to run – which is a common experience on the Raw Beauty Journey. People may be walking and even if they have never run before, they have a sudden urge to do it.

LOOK OUT FOR SIGNS

A few months before the urge to run had seized me. I had met a dynamic woman called Kylie at one of my Raw Food classes. She emailed me a few weeks later to say that the class had completely transformed how she felt about food and how she felt about herself, and that this had made massive positive impacts on her life. If I needed a sports physio who specialised in women, Kylie wanted me to call her so she could return the favour.

So I did just that – I called Kylie and set up an appointment. Now I would see if Kylie thought I could run.

As I sat in the waiting room of her practice, I looked around at the walls and spotted the many Australian sporting teams that had been treated by her and her colleagues.

These athletes came here to look after or rehabilitate their bodies while they played. They did exercises to recover from injury and then they would go on playing. And I suddenly realised that I was now waiting to see if Kylie would give me 'permission' to run. By the time I went in to see her, I had experienced a complete mind shift.

Instead of asking her if she thought I should run. I said, "I am going to run a half marathon in three months and I would like you to tell me what I need to do to make that happen. I will do what you tell me to do."

After having a look she told me it was possible for me to run a half marathon if I did certain exercises. So we went through the routine and I followed exactly what she told me to do for the next three months, and beyond.

I left that room so excited because a self-imposed limitation had been removed. I felt lighter and full of possibility. I was a runner.

THE PASSION FACTOR

I ran my half marathon with no injuries. I ran another half marathon a year later, except 15 minutes faster. A year after that, I ran a 45km ultra marathon with a huge grin on my face.

As a parent, one thing that is always at the forefront of my mind is what I am showing my two children about life's possibilities. Not what I am teaching them, but what I am demonstrating to them.

Just like in the saying, they will do as you do, not as you say. And I am always asking myself, "Who am I being as an example of how life can be? And what will they take into their own lives from how they see me living?"

A living example

I want my children to live with passion, love, fulfilment and connection. And for them to do that, I strongly believe I, as one of their first role models, must be living passion, love, fulfilment and connection for myself. I spent too many years hiding myself and dumbing myself down. But now I see that if I am willing to stand up and live my passions, I am creating a space for others to do the same.

To be self-expressed and able to own who you are is also the most delicious way to live.

CHOOSE PASSION IN LIFE

Over the years I have been cut down again and again, but it affects me less and less now.

In the past when I was hurt I would dive into bed and only come out after a few days if it all seemed safe again – but not before I had put up an internal wall of protection.

However, when we know what our passion is, and when every cell of our being is filled with joy and flow, we are willing and able to take the knocks – because the knocks are a small price to pay for living a passionate life.

Be the light that shines to show a different way of living. Remember that when we step into who we fully are, we allow all the other women around us to do the same – not by telling them what they should be doing, but by being it.

I was given a great visual image of this some time ago that has stuck with me ever since. Two people are standing together, face to face. Person one points their finger in the face of person two. Person two naturally steps back. Person one wags their finger harder, person two steps back and so it goes on. The more and more we try to tell someone what to do, they will step further and further away from us. We may even get pushed back ourselves.

It can be upsetting and make us angry when we are being pushed away, knowing that the information or tools we are offering have the potential to make a huge difference to a person's life. Meeting a wall of resistance can be confusing, but the best way to affect change in another is to affect change in ourselves. Then we can share to our heart's content with willing listeners – and we get to experience ourselves as someone who inspires others.

SHARING WITHIN A COMMUNITY

Sharing our passion and experience is the key; when we do not share with each other, we all feel alone and alienated.

We have the ability to create magical communities as women, coming together to show each other different ways of living and experiencing ourselves. Without this shared sense of community, we keep doing the same things, giving away too much without tending to our own needs, and feeling every other woman is doing a better job than us. We are left feeling empty, burned out, taken for granted, not good enough, disempowered – and then we die. At least we get to lie down then!

EXHAUSTED BY LIFE

I remember at one point being home with my two children when they were both under five years old. We had just moved to Melbourne so I knew nobody and my husband was working long, long days.

I remember thinking, "I wish I could get sick enough so I would have to go to hospital and then I could lie down."

And I am sure that I am not the first mother to have thought that.

It is hard to live a passionate life if we are passionately exhausted. Learning to say yes to ourselves also includes giving energy to ourselves. And that is our best energy – not 'We'll see what's left' energy.

ENERGISED BY PASSION

Every single one of us is entitled to feel passionate and excited about our lives on most days. It will not always be the case because life can be a roller coaster. But to feel passion takes us from surviving our life to living our life.

Never apologise

I have come a long way since the incident at drama school I described in Chapter 2 where I shut off my passion. Sadly, that incident led me to believe that to be inspired and passionate was a bad thing – you would literally get hurt from it.

These days I do not apologise for being passionate. I know that anyone who cannot be around passionate people is not going to choose to be with me. I am passionate with no apologies.

We want passion to become the juice that flows through our bodies and inspires us in all we do and all we stand for. As I have said previously, do not let the dream stealers, the negative whiners or the gossipers take your passion from you.

Nice or passionate?

I spent many years dumbing down my passion to fit in with others. I wanted to be seen as nice and not 'too much'. Now I would rather die with 'She was passionate' as my epitaph rather than 'She was nice'.

What about you? Take the time to work out what you want from your life. In one way it is the biggest thing you will ever create – a blank canvas you get to paint with small brush strokes and massive ones.

When asked what they would ask for if granted one wish, most people say they want a million dollars. When asked why, they have no idea. And that is usually because the dreams and goals we thought we had for our life are actually someone else's.

Do not spend your life trying to turn it into someone else's dream.

CONSIDER YOUR EPITAPH

What will be written on your epitaph? 'She was a good girl'? 'She never upset anyone'? 'She did what was expected of her'?

In her book *The Top Five Regrets of the Dying*, Bronnie Ware says the number one regret is "I wish I'd had the courage to live a life true to myself, not the life others expected of me".

If you knew you would be able to live passionately and still be loved, what would you do? As there are no guarantees, many of us do not take the risk. I had no guarantee that my Thailand boss was who he said he was – I met him once in a pub – but I still took the risk.

My message in this chapter is that if we can learn to be comfortable with being uncomfortable, we will create magic for ourselves and others. But if safe is our main intention for our life, then safe it is, but there is not much magic in safe – and nothing beats the fire that passion ignites.

RAW BEAUTY JOURNEY
Jacinta, 44 years
Senior project administrator

I first saw Kemi on stage at a health seminar I was attending in April 2013. When I look back, I hardly recognise the woman who sat there in the audience watching this dynamic and inspirational woman who spoke about nourishing your beauty from the inside out, and elevating relationships and community.

The woman in the audience that day was empty inside, hiding behind her weight, living a passionless life and trying to shake off the stupor that had overtaken her life. And while I projected to the world a woman who seemed very much in control of her life, inside I was dying.

I was so inspired by Kemi's message – her words and stories were my call to action and so began my Raw Beauty Queen Journey. I will be forever grateful to Kemi and the Raw Beauty Queen programs. In the last 12 months my life and my heart have opened up. I am now experiencing life to the fullest and following my bliss. I am better equipped to handle the ups and down of life, and I am surrounded by a community of Raw Beauties who hold a higher vision for me, and who love me just as I am.

Along the way I softened – not only in my external appearance, but on the inside, too. I learnt that it is okay to be vulnerable, that there is strength in being vulnerable, and by being vulnerable I gave others permission to do the same.

My life had become so small – in 10 years I had not ventured far from my own front door. On my Raw Beauty Journey I learnt that I could expand my world and widen my community without losing who I was. I realised that I had it in me to play a bigger game and play it my way.

I created a beautiful Green Smoothie community in a toxic work environment. I turned my life on its head, and my stinky thinking, too. I went from being disempowered and disenchanted to being empowered and vibrant.

I set myself on a magic carpet ride. I met some of the most extraordinary and amazing women who also happen to be my fellow Raw Beauty Queens. I found my tribe and soul family in the Raw Beauty community, and my place in the world.

I found my passion, my purpose and my contribution – I am a connector and I have a passion for community and helping people. I found the courage to live a life that is congruent with who I am and I separate myself from the pack. I feel back in love with myself, music and my life.

The journey has not always been easy; I have had to face my demons along the way and wage inner war to find peace, courage, strength and joy.

So thank you, Kemi, for your vision.

Living Your Passions Questions

1   What are your passions?
2   What do you need to do to bring more passion into your life?
3   Do you have any fears about passionate living? Are they real?

RAW BEAUTY ACTIONS

Which one can you add today?

4   Declare to three people what your deepest passions are.
5   Book a class, book a seminar, buy a book or do anything that
     nourishes your passion.
6   Say yes to something different – something new.

So you are nourishing your body and feeling good about yourself,
you are nourishing your creative expression, creating your life, and
life is becoming more joyous. You are attracting people into your
life who raise you higher and create a safe environment for you to
be yourself, and living your passion, so what happens next?

10

PRINCIPLE 7
Purpose & Contribution

Nourishment nugget
When we refuse contribution from others we close down their world and ours.

CHOOSE YOUR PURPOSE and then powerfully share it with others in ways that make a difference.

The purpose conundrum

When we have the clarity, energy and passion to see beyond what is happening in our own lives, we start to wonder how we can bring these elements to the lives of others.

Reaching a point in our lives where we are living in alignment with our true nature and our level of self-nourishment is stable and on the up and up, the need and desire to give back is a usual part of the Raw Beauty cycle. But many of us see purpose as a huge mountain to be conquered.

What is my purpose? Why am I here? These are among the biggest life questions we ask ourselves, and the answers have spurred on many women to make a meaningful contribution to other people and the world we live in.

If you are a woman who knows her purpose, then enjoy the ride of fulfilling it. Because when we step into our purpose, it becomes a force of destiny that we cannot ignore, dodge or deny. And if we do try to ignore it, we may find ourselves shouting at our children, arguing with our partners, or both.

Actually, we will probably find ourselves arguing with just about anyone because we need something to do that feels like we are making an impact. I used to do this one all the time: "I need a purpose, and right now that purpose is to make your life unbearable!"

How not to do it

When I was at home with my children all day, I wanted to do other things for myself that expressed who I was. Motherhood is one of the biggest ways we can expand ourselves, but I wanted to expand myself in other areas. So I spent quite some time telling myself I wanted change in this area, but did nothing about it – except to become angry and upset.

I was angry that my husband got to leave the house every day to go to work, so my children got an agitated and not-present mother, and my husband an argumentative and controlling wife.

Oh, we had such fun!

Full speed ahead

When I actually started to create another role for myself with my first business, Food Traditions (which my accountant later called a hobby and told me we could pretend never happened), I felt I had a purpose in addition to that as wife and mother. And everyone was so much happier.

With this new sense of purpose I had so much more to give to my family because I was giving to myself. I was in full creative and expansion mode.

We all need to feel we are of purpose, which looks different for everybody and can change throughout our lifetime.

Where to find purpose

People often travel the world looking for their purpose, and world travel is priceless in what it teaches us about ourselves, as well as about the people of other cultures that inhabit our planet. But it is absolutely possible to find your purpose in your living room.

I believe we already have our purpose – that we are where our purpose is. Our purpose is to step into ourselves.

Who am I?

Take mothers, for example. For some mothers, their purpose is to be at home and raise a family. When the children grow up and leave home, these women need to create another purpose – and if they don't, they may find themselves facing a gaping hole in their life. Which is when their focus may turn to their partner.

"Who are you?" a woman may ask. "I don't even know who you are," she may say. But maybe the question that needs to be said is, "Who am I? I don't know who I am."

Another woman may ask, "Who am I? Am I more than just a mother?" Or for women who are not mothers, it can be, "Who am I? Am I me or what I have been told to be?"

And for all women, no matter what their life circumstances, we can ask, "I have ticked all the right boxes and achieved so much, but who am I?"

These are all fantastic questions that can lead us on a wonderful path of discovery, expansion and creation. And they are questions that need to be asked – and answered. But some women can be paralysed by the "Who am I?" question because it is such a huge one, and all to do with purpose.

My purpose and how it changes

Was acting my purpose? I know and have experienced the telling of stories as a profound way of making a difference and a contribution. But even though the telling of stories is one of the highest and most respected art forms, I knew that my purpose was not acting.

When I was first working as a chef, my purpose was to make food for people, but the first kitchen I was employed in was not much more than a junk food establishment. So when I became more aware of my values and the direction in which I wanted to go, I decided not to work in just any kitchen, and my direction and purpose changed.

When I was working at The Organic Cafe in London, my purpose was to make nourishing food for people who also nourished the planet. And when I moved to an upmarket restaurant in London's Kensington, it was to support producers and farmers of high integrity, and to utilise their produce in the best way I could.

My purpose in each of these jobs changed and evolved as I changed and evolved. So when I launched Kemi's Raw Kitchen, my purpose was to inspire people to 'add more raw' to their lives with joy and passion. And that has led me to launch Raw Beauty Queen, where my purpose is to empower women to nourish their unique, beautiful selves.

So you see how purpose changes.

Choose in the moment

Within the Raw Beauty philosophy, we choose our purpose and contribution in the moment by asking the following questions:

1   How can I be of purpose right now?
2   How can I contribute right now?
3   How can I allow others to contribute to me right now?

Framing the questions in this way takes away the pressure and possible paralysis that comes with asking, "What is my purpose in life?"

You are here, I say, so choose something – for now.

Every moment of each day we are choosing, whether consciously or not, even when we are choosing not to choose!

Knowing that we can be of purpose in the here and now is an empowering concept. It means we always have a purpose – it is nothing to search or wait for. It is already here.

Taking purposeful actions on a daily basis naturally leads us to feeling more purposeful generally, ready to contribute whenever needed and wherever we are. And some of us may discover an ultimate purpose through these small daily actions.

The gift of contribution

I remember when I was having a really bad day, everything felt hard to do and it all seemed pointless and looked to be getting no better. Then one of my closest friends called me, and her day was going even worse. In fact, it was so bad that when I picked up the phone to answer her call, all I could hear was her crying.

I knew how she was feeling – I had been the sobbing caller many times. So we chatted about what was going on for her, and I listened and contributed some thoughts. She thanked me and we ended the call. But what she did not realise was that by allowing me to contribute to her, she had gotten me out of my slump.

Supporting her had removed my head from my own bottom, and to be in someone else's world gave me perspective on mine.

A few months later, I called her in an upset state and the reverse happened – she thanked me because in contributing to me, I gave her a purpose.

We get so wrapped up in not being a burden to each other, but we need each other to give purpose and contribution all the time. And there are so many ways to have purpose and contribution in our lives.

What do you want to give?

In the great contribution and purpose exchange, how do we want to make others feel? A great way to tap into the meaning of this question is to think about the predominant feeling we like to experience for ourselves on most days. Is it love? Or maybe it is happiness, peace, connection, fun, freedom or calm?

Whatever it is, we can choose to bring these feelings to others – this can be our purpose and our contribution. And carrying this same feeling around with us can also dictate to whom, what and how we contribute.

This is how it works. If we choose love as our purpose, this means when we see someone fall over in the street, we help them up because we want them to experience love.

If we choose freedom as our purpose, when a girlfriend is struggling with her children's demands, we babysit for her so that she can experience freedom.

So just because our purpose is not to save the rainforests (unless it is, and please go and do that because the planet is waiting for you) it does not mean you are not purposeful. It does not mean that you have nothing to contribute. You may never know how your actions affected the stranger who fell.

Your girlfriend will return to her children, but the sense of freedom she experienced may now allow her to give herself permission to take more 'freedom time'.

Our purpose does not have to mean building an orphanage in a remote land – although there is a great need for that, for some people the task is just too big. But if that sounds like something you would like to do, realise that anyone who has ever built an orphanage in a faraway land had absolutely no idea how to do it until they took an action and started.

The individuality of contributing

We are all drawn to completely different ways of contributing, and thankfully there is so much contribution needed we will never be turned away. There can never be too many contributors on this planet.

No one else on the entire planet can do what you can do or contribute like you do. No one else has had your life experiences or your dreams. No one can make a difference in exactly the same way you can.

So we do not have to spend time navel-gazing to 'find our purpose' because, as I said previously, we are our purpose. And how we contribute is a personal decision.

CONTRIBUTING TO MY MARRIAGE

One of my biggest contributions is to my marriage. I know that if my husband and I can nourish our marriage, we can handle everything else we need to. When we are struggling, I struggle. Not because I cannot live without him (I am a modern woman, after all), but because I have chosen my relationship with him as the most important in my life. It is the foundation of all my relationships.

A few years ago a woman wrote in *TIME* magazine that she loved her husband more than she loved her children, and there was mass outrage. How could a mother say such a thing?! Well, I completely got it.

It is not that I love my husband more than my children, but the love I feel for my husband is not comparable to the love I feel for my children. If I had not met and fallen in love with my husband, our children would not be here to love.

Also, I know that it makes a difference to my children when their mummy and daddy are in harmony. And I hope that we contribute to them a positive experience of love and partnership.

As well as showing our children what a great marriage built on love, connection and growth looks like, we also love contributing to the marriages and relationships around us. And these friends in turn contribute to and support our marriage.

LET PURPOSE INSPIRE YOUR CONTRIBUTION

For you, purpose may be feeding the homeless, while someone else may choose to contribute by sharing their music with the world.

In my student days a friend and I walked past a woman collecting for a children's charity. My friend put some money into the container and I did not, and she asked me angrily why I did not want to donate to that charity. When I explained that homelessness and AIDS had affected my life, and that I wanted to contribute my time and money in those areas, she was not impressed. But I was not trying to impress her.

We should never allow anyone else to make us feel bad about how and where we choose to contribute our time, money or resources. They are ours to give to whomever and however we decide. And we know we are on the right path when making the contribution fills us up as well as benefiting the recipient. But a person is not on the right path if they are left feeling drained, resentful or used, and the other is left feeling disempowered, a victim, tolerated or resentful.

Helping versus contributing

There can be a big difference between helping someone and contributing to them.

Helping can mean that we have an investment in the outcome and are wounded if the recipient does not do what we suggest.

I raise my hand as a former 'helper' who used to get so upset that after spending hours listening to and talking with a friend about issues they were facing, they did not take my good advice! I would be secretly very disappointed when nine times out of 10 my help was not put to use.

But it feels great to let go of this 'helping' mentality. Contributing feels so much healthier and better for both parties.

When we choose to contribute to someone, we are giving freely because that is what is in our heart to do. We are not attached to what they decide to do with what we have contributed to them. We are happy to be there for them, but contribution is giving out of generosity and keeps both parties on an equal footing.

Because of my heritage, I have always wanted to contribute to Africa in a way that was not patronising or would not undermine those to whom I wanted to contribute. For a long time I looked for something that, as an African woman, I could be involved in that had empowerment and integrity at its base – I like to feel empowered and that is how I want other women to feel.

When I came across the work of The Hunger Project, I knew it was what I had been looking for. What follows is part of their view on empowering women in developing countries, which appears on their website.

> "We believe that the poor, illiterate women are the key to ending world hunger. When given a voice, these women become powerful and important change-agents in raising their families and their villages out of poverty. Unlocking the creativity, leadership, entrepreneurialism and productivity of the poorest of the poor is what we do. We build leaders. We especially build women leaders."
> – *The Hunger Project*

When I visited Uganda with women's network Business Chicks™ to see the work of The Hunger Project, I was humbled, inspired, empowered and grateful. So many of the women I met were changing their own lives in extraordinary ways. They were empowered, they had vision and they were unstoppable in situations most of us, in our positions of relative privilege, would find impossible to deal with – considering we have food, shelter and medical care, and we are not at risk of being sold by our parents, mutilated or not being educated because we are women.

One woman had watched her nine adult children die of AIDS and now looked after her orphaned grandchildren in a tiny one-room mud-brick home with minimal resources. Some of her grandchildren decided she was pretty hopeless at looking after them (she was understandably in deep grief), so they left and went to the city to find some work.

She told us she had nothing to live for and had been waiting to die. But once she began The Hunger Project training, she had something to live for – she created her own vision and then took action.

She started with a micro loan and proceeded to build herself and her remaining grandchildren a new home. Her previous home became her storage room and kitchen, and she said she liked to look at the storage room from her new house so she could see what she had achieved.

She was now putting all of her grandchildren through school and, when asked what she was going to do next, she pointed up to the banana-leaf roof on her new home and said, "I am going to put a tin roof on my house. I have something to live for now." And she was smiling from ear to ear.

Self-nourished giving works best

Just a final word about contribution – if we want to contribute to friends, family or the community, we need to do so when our self-nourishment levels are high because it is hard to give generously or abundantly to others when it given is with resentment or anger or out of duty. If the contribution is given in a resentful way, the person we want to contribute to will feel bad and conflicted because of it.

Choose a purpose in each moment

We do things all the time that are of purpose, even if we may not be aware of it. And to create a purpose within our present life means we are not waiting until life is perfect to do so.

Today I have been of purpose getting my children to school, being a listening ear for a friend, being a creative contributor to a fundraising project, connecting two businesses that will work in partnership together, listened to my son's viola practice and read with my daughter – and that was just in the past five hours of the day. Soon my purpose will be to fall asleep.

Chances are, if you listed the purposes you have chosen today, your list will be as fulfilling as mine.

Learn to say YES

Do you find it easy to allow people to contribute to you? I used to find it really hard because I felt I would be a burden on people. I thought needing help was weak and I sometimes thought I could do it better.

When I was in my early 20s, my acting career and an inheritance from my foster grandmother Christine afforded me my first home. Because I had been moved around so much as a child, this was a very, very big deal for me. This was the first home I could not be moved from unless I said so.

My foster father and I spent many months doing it up and converting it from a one-bedroom flat to a two-bedroom one so that I could have a lodger to help pay the mortgage.

I was lucky enough to have two great friends stay in succession over the first two years or so, and I used to throw some very good parties. In fact, I made a lot of effort to create the best party I could.

The first year I had my birthday party there I was exhausted with the preparations and the morning of my party my flatmate heard me crying. When she asked me what was wrong I said, "I am so exhausted because no one has helped me do this party – I have done it all on my own. I have made all the food, the invitations and the cake, and I have cleaned and shopped all on my own."

So my flatmate did a great job of cheering me up and we finished the preparations together.

Next year, different flatmate, same scenario and same response. But the following year the flatmate was my sister and I got a very different response. As I blubbed that no one had helped me arrange my party, she replied, "You never ask anyone to bloody help you. And when people do help, you are not satisfied with their efforts, as they are not up to your standard. So people have just stopped offering."

Ouch. She was right. I had taken on my second foster mother's mantra – if you want a job done properly, do it yourself – but it had left me exhausted and, to be honest, lonely. And it had left the people around me unable to contribute to me, or weary and tense if they tried.

I now live on the other side. I ask for help and support all of the time, whether it is personal or for business or pleasure.

There is nothing like contributing to someone else – I love it and now I would never want to stop others having that feeling.

I have also realised that my 'standards' or 'expectations' are mine alone, and not a stick by which I can measure others.

I am now happy and grateful to take contribution when it is offered. I always try to say yes. If I feel someone is offering from a place of 'should', I will check in with them.

The truth is, we all want to feel like we make a difference to someone – that we are of value.

We all need a purpose. We all need others to contribute to us. We all need to contribute to others.

RAW BEAUTY JOURNEY
Joy, 62 years
Myotherapist

When a friend invited me to a Raw Beauty seminar, I felt quite dismissive and cynical. Why should I go? I had no body issues, loved my husband and family, felt well and optimistic, exercised consistently, ate healthily and worked in an area that gave me great satisfaction. But... why was I always so damn busy? And didn't this periodically tip over into me feeling exhausted, resentful of all my responsibilities and then being forced to a complete stop by days in bed with the flu or some other illness? Then I'd recover, leap up and continue with my high-energy, busy life – until the next time...

I began to see this was an unhelpful repetitive pattern that I just seemed stuck in and didn't know how to change. When I heard Kemi say, "I want to help you put yourself on your own to-do list" I knew this was what I needed to do.

I'm 62 years old and I thought, in 20 years I'll be in my 80s, and do I want to review my life from there and think, "Why did I rush around so much and just race through this precious life?"

I knew this was the time to plan the next stage of my life... and immediately I started to sabotage myself.

Why go on a retreat with other women when I would probably enjoy myself more trekking the Annapurna Circuit or even walking the Kokoda Trail? Hadn't I always loved being active, on-the-go and pushing myself?" And on and on it went, as I talked myself out of it. Until my daughter said, "Mum, you need to do this to show me how to look after myself and give away less of myself to others. You're my role model in this."

After that, there was no looking back.

Although, I was then shocked to discover I was afraid of not being busy. Who would I be? Would I be boring or bored? Would I become dull and insipid – someone people wouldn't want to be around? Well, it was time to find out.

The retreat with Kemi was life-changing and wonderful, as I allowed myself to slow down, reflect and immerse myself in the processes. The doubts and fears fell away one by one, and I got glimpses of myself that I had never seen before, despite having done lots of self-development work and self-analysis.

Kemi's ability to be intuitive, incredibly earthy and grounded and to provide wise and wonderful experience made the retreat a transformative experience. Her ability to distil the Raw Beauty Principles into bite-size pieces allows them to impact your life immediately. You can make commitments that empower you because they're not more than you can realistically manage.

This is no impossible pie-in-the-sky set of principles, but a series of highly pragmatic and achievable guidelines that enable you to be the best you can be.

I'm still highly energetic and busy, but somehow some space has opened up so I have more choice than I used to have. I know how to say no when it doesn't serve me, and yes to new opportunities and ideas outside of my comfort zone.

I have new goals and plans for this next stage of my life, and this makes me feel energised and fully alive. I know it won't all be sweet and trouble-free, but I feel capable of dealing with whatever life throws my way and making the most of each day.

Thank you, Kemi.

Purpose & Contribution Questions

1 What is your purpose today?
2 How would you like to contribute to the wider world?
3 Where can you say yes to contribution from someone else?

RAW BEAUTY ACTIONS

Which one can you add today?

1 This week, make a contribution calendar and list seven people who you are going to joyfully contribute to. One for each day.
2 Make a phone call and volunteer your time to a charity.
3 Volunteer yourself to a family member or friend as their right-hand woman for a half or whole day. If she wants to sort her wardrobe, help her. If she wants to plant a vegie patch, help her. Whatever she wants, help her.

———————————

You are nourishing your body and feeling good about yourself. You are nourishing your creative expression and creating your life, which is becoming more joyous. You are attracting people who raise you higher and create a safe environment for you to be yourself, you are living your passion, and now you are living with purpose. So what happens next?

11

RAW BEAUTY QUEEN TESTIMONIALS

THE BEST WAY for you to see the potential for Raw Beauty in your life is through reading about how others have found and used it.

You are about to read the testimonials of six women. Each of the women sharing their Raw Beauty Journeys here are of different ages, live in different countries and work in different areas. Some have children, some do not; some are married, some are not. Each of them has either participated in a Raw Beauty Queen Retreat or The Raw Beauty Queen Lifestyle Program.

Each came to Raw Beauty from different starting points, but are all experiencing the effects of peeling back the layers to reveal who they really are and what they want to create for themselves and in their lives.

Bronwyn Craig, 60 years
Primary school teacher

I feel so fortunate, honoured, privileged and blessed to have been a participant in The Raw Beauty Queen Program. I first met Kemi at a Raw Beauty Queen weekend in Melbourne. I was impressed with her vitality and energy and her passion for all women to feel beautiful and good about themselves.

The weekend was not enough for me – Kemi had ignited a huge fire in my body and I wanted to spend more time with her and to learn more. I knew that I needed help and this followed with a magical week in Bali with Kemi and 11 other beautiful women.

Before The Raw Beauty Queen Lifestyle Program I was in survival mode. I was sad, and felt neglected and overworked. My nerves were overloaded and at breaking point.

Who was I? I was someone's daughter, someone's sister, someone's wife, someone's mother, someone's relation, someone's friend and someone's employee. I felt I had to be there for everyone in the best capacity I could, even – and which I was unaware of then – to the detriment of my mental and physical wellbeing.

What was I? I felt neglected, a victim, a doormat and a servant who certainly did not have any boundaries.

With the beautiful, gentle, wise mentoring of Kemi, these feelings shifted.

Kemi guided, challenged, uplifted and inspired me to realise and create the life I wanted – a life of peace and tranquillity, a life fulfilled with happiness, laughter and passion. A life where I didn't feel guilty about having time for me. A life where I was independent and felt okay about the decisions I made. A life where I didn't have to get everyone's approval and be concerned about what people thought.

With encouragement and the realisation that I had an opinion and a choice, I was able to make changes and take action in the way I felt about my life and myself.

My self-esteem has grown and I feel so much more confident. I now do little and big things for myself and, without feeling selfish, have been able to say no and set better boundaries that enable me to take better care of myself. I am able to step out of my comfort zone and feel the fear and do it anyway. I only have one life and I need to live it to the fullest.

I am so much happier, relaxed and more at peace. I feel good about myself and know that I am special, unique and that I have much to offer.

Others have noticed the change in me. My journey is ongoing, and I take action on a daily basis to nourish my life and myself.

Thank you, beautiful Kemi, for challenging and helping me to get to know myself and for introducing me to the 7 Principles of Raw Beauty.

What a huge impact and difference one lady can make!

Paula, 44 years

Loving my children, supporting my husband, creating a
welcoming home and nurturing possibilities in others

At the time Kemi introduced me to the 7 Principles of Raw Beauty, it was four months since I had moved countries with my husband and two sons, aged four and two years. I was feeling tired, I was feeling 'old', I was shouting at my boys, I was missing my friends, I was missing the purpose and contribution that my previous volunteering had given me, I was struggling with being a full-time mum, and I was feeling guilty and ungrateful about struggling with being a full-time mum. All of this wrapped up in wanting to support my family in settling into a new country, wanting to support my son's transition to preschool, and wanting to fully embrace the adventure of living in a different country.

When I started applying the 7 Principles of Raw Beauty to my life, Principle 1 – Body Nourishment – was the easiest way for me to reconnect with myself. To get up at 6am every morning was not easy, as I was still having broken sleep, but it made the rest of my day much smoother emotionally.

Adding the Green Smoothie didn't appear to do anything at first, but now a year or so on my energy levels are way more consistent. Adding more raw in terms of salads made me laugh because I was in the middle of a Canadian winter with temperatures of minus 20 or so outside.

The main reason I joined Kemi on her course was to explore and discover what my passion is and how to engage life with more purpose and contribution. I didn't clarify that during the course. However, what I did get was a much greater degree of comfort sitting with the uncertainty of not knowing.

The desperateness I initially felt around this dissipated.

Looking back, I can see that living the 7 Principles of Raw Beauty has definitely helped me in many ways. Now I plan to do one thing a day that I really enjoy. I focus on expressing gratitude to those around me regularly. I consciously choose to invest in supportive relationships – meditating with my boys when I put them to sleep, a monthly date with my husband, a weekly phone call with my father, regular phone calls with my friends, a monthly 'sanity' dinner with my new friends. The principles have helped me become more comfortable being outside of my comfort zone. I now consciously take on things that challenge me and scare me. I started learning Spanish. I ask for what I would like.

I'm organising a festival to celebrate and give people the opportunity to take action on International Day of the Girl. This is at times very overwhelming, but I keep coming back to the question – if I wasn't scared, what would I do? And building awareness of the issues that girls from all around the world face is one of those things.

A heartfelt thank you Kemi, for the opportunity and the tools to fully embrace my life, and to help me be me, unapologetically.

Catheryn, 34 years
Registered midwife, training shiatsu therapist

Firstly, I would like to say a big thank you with all of my heart to Kemi, for supporting me in taking charge of my life to steer it in the direction I want it to go.

I completed The Raw Beauty Queen Lifestyle Program, where I learned about the 7 Principles of Raw Beauty and began implementing these very powerful concepts in my life daily. All I can say is, wow! What I really loved about the 7 Principles is the way they were ordered so thoughtfully to flow gently from one to the next. When I got to the end of the program it all clicked, and I realised the importance of embodying each principle in turn as I went along.

Before I began working with Kemi, I was feeling lost and stuck in a rut. I was working in a profession that I was no longer enjoying nor had a passion for, and it was having a major adverse effect on my health. Moving away from it seemed frightening and unimaginable – I thought by making such a big change, my world would come crashing down around me. I knew I needed to change things, but didn't know where to begin or how. I was getting more anxious and unwell each day.

When I first heard Kemi speak, I was drawn to her. I was absolutely blown away by her passion, energy and sense of humour. I was sitting there thinking, "I want some of what she's got – I wonder how I can get it…" Ha ha, now I know.

With Kemi's support and guidance, I found the courage to leave my career and at the same time turn my fears, anxieties and uncertainty into empowerment and excitement for the new life I am creating. And my world has not come crashing down – just the opposite.

Since working with Kemi and following the 7 Principles of Raw Beauty, it has made such a massive difference to my life and I am so grateful. I have grown so much. I love my new-found confidence in myself, and love that I'm not as fearful to get out of my comfort zone and have a go. I now see myself in a whole other light. I am now also making better food choices.

Principle 1 – Body Nourishment – would have to be my favourite. Adding more raw and living plant foods has given me an amazing amount of extra energy. This then increased my motivation and gave me clarity I had not felt in a long time. The brain fog subsided. And Principle 1 really set me up well to progress into the following Raw Beauty Principles. I found that when I was taking care of myself, I was much more able to support others.

I am truly blessed to have Kemi in my life. My appreciation and admiration for her are indescribable. I cannot wait to continue my work with her and see the amazing changes to come.

Anwen, 26 years
Freelance writer and nanny

Before embarking on the Raw Beauty Queen Weekend (RBQW), I was struggling with an injury that had overtaken my mind, body and life. I had been on painkillers every day for over two years and this, and the injury itself, really affected my sense of self and where I was going in my life – not that I even had the foresight to see this at the time. I was completely immersed in the pain, but without any control over it. Pain was all I knew.

Then I was given the wonderful gift of a ticket to RBQW at the beautiful Abbotsford Convent.

I walked in with no expectations, a little bit of fear and a whole lot of curiosity. And I got blown away. Being in a room with just women going through the 7 Principles of Raw Beauty was powerful. The shared experiences and feelings brought us together as a community with so many gifts we didn't even know we shared. The dark cloud of pain hanging over me wasn't a point of shame – it was something to be proud of.

I had been in incredible pain and Western medicine had been pumped through me for years as the doctors tried to find some sort of normalcy, until the drugs no longer worked. And yet here I was, surrounded by other emotionally aware human beings who were proud of me and my journey, marvelling at my achievements and nurturing me through the 7 Principles that were quickly changing the way I looked at myself, and my outlook on life.

Principle 2 – Self-Love – threw me into a few loops. Having been so focused on the physical realm of my life, I had left the rest behind. And then, all of a sudden, Kemi was telling me to take care of myself?! I had been living day-to-day for so long just trying to 'be normal' that loving myself seemed like a foreign concept.

Principle 5 – Elevating Relationships & Communities – had a profound effect on me. I had no idea what I was allowed to want from my relationships, so I kept on giving it to others in the hope that someone might see what I actually needed and want to give it to me in return. This principle not only made me realise there was a disparity in many of my relationships, it made me see how my actions needed to change. Rather than hoping that someone might be able to read my mind one day, I had to take control and ask for what I wanted from others. I needed to communicate with those around me.

I went off the last of my painkillers in the following months, with just my Vitamix juicer, Green Smoothies and new frame of mind as my support. This was something I had been working on with my army of doctors over the previous six months, and it seemed so easy to achieve in the end after learning how kickass women are.

What I learnt from the RBQW was to stop selling myself short and embrace who I am, and the makeover that then happened in my personal life was massive. I am now able to give myself 'treats' – like a nice hot bath after a long day. I surround myself with people who bring out the best in me, and I am not afraid to ask to be nurtured, to face criticism from people I respect or to argue for what I think is right.

Anne, 49 years
Office Manager

The 7 Principles of Raw Beauty have supported me to explore my beliefs. Principles 1, 5, 6 and 7 – Body Nourishment, Elevating of Relationships & Communities, Living Your Passions, and Purpose & Contribution – have supported me in becoming very clear about my journey this lifetime.

I am a very kind, giving person, but I have realised I wasn't nourishing myself first, so I expected things in return when I helped other people. I now make time to nourish my body with food, exercise and dancing, and I now have more unconditional love to give to others because I have loved and appreciated myself first.

I never knew what I wanted to be when I grew up. The Purpose & Contribution Principle supported me in becoming very clear about my purpose.

Through the challenges I have experienced in my life, I will be able to create a safe and empowering space for other women to face their fears and feel gratitude for their journey.

I feel so loved and supported by my Raw Beauty Queen Community – magic happens when we are safe and supported to get out of our comfort zones.

Kemi has supported me in writing my personal mission statement, which gives me courage every day to say I AM ME:

I was born to create a safe, magical space for humanity, and I will do this by dancing with my fears into the sunshine.

Linda, 35 years
Health and wellness crusader

My health and wellness journey began with one of the greatest loves of my life – food! We haven't always been the best of pals, however, and it's been a long and bumpy road to get us to where we are today.

In the past I constantly worried about whether people liked me so I could never fully relax and be myself. I was always comparing myself to the other girls who were 'perfect' and didn't seem to have a care in the world.

This lead to my involvement in a variety of destructive activities and behaviours as a way to numb out, and also included a very unhealthy relationship with food. I couldn't control what was going on inside my head, but I could control what I was putting into my body or, should I say, what I wasn't. I based my self-worth on how I looked on the outside, so I restricted my food intake in order to measure up to society's ideals.

This period caused me a new level of instability, stress and anxiety because now I was depending on someone else for my happiness and, more often than not, I would be left feeling unsatisfied, disappointed and terribly miserable and empty.

Like my relationships, my eating habits became extreme and I oscillated between nourishing myself with clean and wholesome foods that made me feel amazing, to all-out binges on 'bad' foods that made me feel ill. When I had these reckless, compulsive moments, I would berate myself for being weak and out of control. Food was either my best ally or my worst enemy.

I was instantly captivated by Kemi's charisma and light-heartedness, and found her to be so engaging. She was bursting with energy and vitality, and everything she spoke of resonated with me. Clearly she was walking the walk and living her truth. I loved her honest, balanced and practical approach, and knew this was someone I wanted to connect with.

Kemi developed the 7 Principles of Raw Beauty and I was completely sold – here was a comprehensive but simple and well-thought-out system that could help any woman reach her full potential.

I was particularly interested in the Principle of Body Nourishment because of my struggles in the past. Although it was still presenting issues for me, I had come a long way in this area through a lot of self-enquiry and inner work, but Kemi helped me look at body nourishment from another perspective – that it was ultimately a form of self-love.

I realised that if ever I was going to make peace with my relationship with food and my body, I had to first fill myself up with love. It reinforced to me the importance of self-love because without it, we can't live the life we deserve and be who we need to be in this world.

Principle 6 – Living Your Passions – also struck a chord because I had been feeling stuck in administrative-type roles that didn't challenge or stimulate me, and this was consequently affecting my feelings of self-worth. I had been wanting to make the transition to a more fulfilling career in the health and wellness industry, but was too scared to step out of my comfort zone and felt I lacked the knowledge and skills to succeed.

I had stopped myself from trying new things and ventures many times in the past for fear of failing. Kemi made me realise that I have the ability to achieve anything I set my mind to, and that I am doing the world as well a myself a disservice if I'm not living my passion and sharing my gift with others.

Since adding these principles to my life, I am a lot more forgiving and nurturing towards myself. I still have those little voices in my head, but when a negative thought creeps in or I detect something about my personality that makes me feel uncomfortable, I take more of a curious approach and ask where that thought is stemming from and why that is coming up for me. I now use it as a driver for self-improvement and transformation.

I am also putting myself out there a bit more, trying new activities and behaviours that I previously would have been too fearful or reluctant to attempt. Even seemingly small acts have given me a sense of achievement and confidence to delve into other activities that will enrich my life

I no longer see food as a means for control or something to fill a void, but as a way to nourish my body, mind and soul so I can operate at full capacity and get that little bit closer to serving my purpose.

Now that I have turned a corner with my relationship with food and myself, I feel ready to let down the barriers and invite someone special back into my life again. Kemi has given me the confidence to believe that I am capable of having a healthy relationship, and the courage to seek out that person who I can physically, mentally, emotionally and spiritually connect with.

Finally, I must also make reference to Principle 5 – Elevating Relationships & Communities – and give a shout out to all my Raw Beauty Queens, for whom I am so grateful and love so dearly. I have been extremely blessed to have had many wonderful and influential women in my life who have nurtured and supported me through all my challenges, and have helped shape the person I am today. Like Kemi, I also believe that when we join forces, women can do amazing things!

12
RAW BEAUTY
IN A NUTSHELL

I HOPE YOU have experienced a gentle but powerful form of nourishment as you worked through this book and its Raw Beauty Actions. And with that self-nourishment germinating, I hope many new exciting possibilities opened up for you along the way.

My wish for you

I wish for you an expanded sense of yourself, and hope that you have allowed self-love and self-care to take their rightful position of honour at the top of your to-do list.

My desire for you is to have begun to grasp that your beauty is in your own hands, and that who you are and your contribution to the world is where your Raw Beauty lives.

Sometimes in life we sit down and wonder why things are not going how we want them to. We say life is not fair and ask if it is ever going to get better. Well, I hope you have seen that whether life is fair or not makes no difference to the outcome, and whether and when things get better, well, that is completely up to you…

Shifting and sharing

I want to remind you that rather than staying safe and only living at 15 per cent of our full potential, through slowly adding the Raw Beauty Actions, one by one, consistently and wholeheartedly, we can shift what is stopping us reach 100 per cent of our potential – and not only in ourselves, but in the people around us.

If you have committed to the Raw Beauty Actions as you have read this book, I trust that you have already been experiencing aspects of this shift as you have gone from principle to principle. And I remind you that when we continue to nourish ourselves and share our journeys with other women, we are giving them permission to increase their self-nourishment, joy, passion and Raw Beauty.

One day after a hot yoga class, I was changing next to an older woman in her late 50s, and our conversation went like this.

Her: This yoga is great. When I first came I could hardly function all day, I was so tired. Now I am jumping out of my skin with energy. I feel so good. I have to keep it to myself, though, because people won't like it.

Me: You are feeling great, so shout out about it!

Her: No. It is all right for you – you are young. When you are older, people are angrier, with no energy and so to share that I am older but feeling great is seen as arrogant.

Me: What? No! Shout it out so that you become the new standard they can aspire to.

Her: You mean show off about it?

Me: No, be authentically you. Share your joys and do not apologise for living and creating a life that makes you feel good.

The inspiring words of spiritual teacher and author Marianne Williamson say it the best:

> "Our deepest fear is not that we are inadequate. Our deepest fear is that we are powerful beyond measure. It is our light, not our darkness that most frightens us. We ask ourselves, Who am I to be brilliant, gorgeous, talented, fabulous? Actually, who are you not to be? You are a child of God. Your playing small does not serve the world. There is nothing enlightened about shrinking so that other people won't feel insecure around you. We are all meant to shine, as children do. We were born to make manifest the glory of God that is within us. It's not just in some of us; it's in everyone. And as we let our own light shine, we unconsciously give other people permission to do the same. As we are liberated from our own fear, our presence automatically liberates others."
>
> – MARIANNE WILLIAMSON, *A Return to Love*

Instead of living from a place of what will they think of me, the more important question becomes what I think of me. Be convinced that it is possible for you to be nourished, fulfilled, passionate and successful; that you can love yourself and others, contribute to the planet and make a difference.

Of course, you will still have days when it does not go to plan – we all have bad days – but at the foundation of it all, the 7 Principles of Raw Beauty will carry you forward, supporting the continued growth of your self-love each day. And as your self-love increases, the world inside and outside of you becomes a different place.

The Raw Beauty Queen Manifesto

With your Raw Beauty in action, you get to create a life of possibility, expansion, passion, joy and connection. And my message to you will always be, you are beautiful – nourish yourself! And always remember the Raw Beauty Queen Manifesto:

I am unique and beautiful.

I take daily steps to honour myself and my life

with nourishing words and actions.

I elevate myself and all other women.

I am a Raw Beauty Queen.

Raw eating recap

The foundation of the Raw Beauty Journey is how we choose to fuel and nourish our bodies – which, as you have seen, impacts on everything else in our lives. But how much raw is there in Raw Beauty?

Well, how much raw food we decide to add is completely up to us, and it will change and shift as much as we and the seasons do.

When I first started eating raw foods I kept it very simple – adding a big plate of salad or two every day – but then I began to experiment with more complex methods of preparing raw foods, like dehydrating and fermenting.

Depending on what I am doing and the season, sometimes I eat raw all day but some days, such as in winter, I begin with a large Green Smoothie or juice and then the rest of my food is cooked.

As I have mentioned throughout this book, there are no 'shoulds' in Raw Beauty – and that gives us the freedom to experiment with what works for us, and when we do it.

What I do know is that I will never return to a life of eating just cooked food, day after day after day because it makes me feel heavy, blocked, tired and cloudy.

For simple and flavour-filled raw food recipes to add to your life, check out my free recipes at www.keminekvapil.com.

The Raw Sisterhood Roar!

Beyond the food, there is more to Raw Beauty – the roar and power of sisterhood.

Raw Beauty is about uplifting and supporting each other, because no matter where we come from, the colour of our skin, how old we are, how our past has played out and how our present looks, we are all of us in this together.

Roar with Raw Beauty if you, like me, want to see a world where young women do not believe their worth is in becoming the 'numb and dumb good girl'; if you, like me, are sick of the sexualisation of girls; if you, like me, are devastated by the universal disempowerment of women in its many forms; and if you, like me, are wanting a new paradigm for future generations to step into.

We must roar our collective Raw Beauty out loud because future generations of women are counting on us!

Hear me roar...

So where has my Raw Journey taken me? I explained my beginnings, background and discovery of Raw Beauty in Chapter 2, and thought you may want to know what has happened for me since. I hope my journey paints a picture of what is possible when we step in, step up and step out.

RAW BEAUTY JOURNEY
Kemi, 40 years
Speaker and wellness coach

Before the start of my Raw Beauty Journey, I was scared most of the time.

I believed everything I saw on TV or read in the newspaper – I believed the world was a very bad and scary place where beautiful things happened sometimes.

I was a control freak. I was afraid that if I could not control my whole environment, things would fall apart – including me.

I never showed my vulnerabilities, which gave people the impression I was strong and that I did not need anything – which made me resentful and needy.

Life just happened to me. I was a victim waiting for the next slap in the face to come my way. And when the slap came, I became stronger in the sense of becoming more disconnected, closing my heart more, building another internal wall and trying to make life as small as possible. It was safer that way.

My only personal values involved other people liking me, so I shifted and morphed depending on who I was with. This left me confused and exhausted from constantly walking on eggshells – just trying to survive each day and each interaction.

Since my Raw Beauty Journey began, I have transformed practically every area of my life. Not because I felt I needed to (I was doing fine as a controlling, closed-off, scared person, thanks), but because as I took each step on the journey, other steps made themselves apparent to me and I took them, one by one.

I have travelled to over 20 countries, which is huge for me because after living at Nan's my insect phobia was so bad I would not even go to the park because I knew there were insects there. (I choose to have therapy to manage that phobia, so that I can travel the world for pleasure and work.)

I am now married with two children. (I never wanted either, but am very happy with both, thanks.)

I moved from London to Melbourne, Australia, and fostered myself out with my in-laws for three and a half years. (My seventh set of parents – greedy, I know!)

I had two extraordinary homebirths. (I did not control them.)

I am a marathon runner. (I was told and believed I could not run.)

I look in the mirror and am very happy with what I see. (I overate, constantly compared myself to others and had no idea how to nourish my body.)

I have a purpose, which is to be part of a movement of women who nourish themselves and each other to create lives that make a difference.

I live with passion flowing through me, I get to speak and coach women to stand in their unique and beautiful power. (I believed I would be hurt if I put my hand up.)

I am an author. (I thought people like me do not write books.)

I am responsible for my life. I create my life, moment by moment, and I am proud of what I have created so far.

Everything began from adding more raw food to my life. The energy, clarity and nourishment it gives me fuel everything I do.

Now when I look at the world, I see a beauty-filled place, where bad things sometimes happen.

I love where I live. x

13
WHAT IS NEXT FOR YOU?

So now you are nourishing your body and feeling good about yourself. You are nourishing your creative expression and creating your life, which is becoming more joyous. You are attracting people who raise you higher and create a safe environment for you to be yourself. You are living your passions, and you are living with purpose. So what happens next?

This is up to you.

Let's be honest – the easiest thing for you would be to put this book away on a shelf. But the most powerful thing would be to read it again and take on different Raw Beauty Actions, or to pass it on to a friend so they can ignite their own Raw Beauty.

My aim is for this book to take women to a place where we can safely nourish our unique beauty, inside and out, and be ourselves without apology or fear.

May we support each other to be the most beautiful and empowered versions of ourselves!

There are many more ways for you to enhance your Raw Beauty Journey further, and to get the beautiful women in your life involved as well.

RAW BEAUTY ACTION

If you want to experience more Raw Beauty, please visit

www.keminekvapil.com

to find an abundance of Raw Beauty waiting for you including:

Free Raw Beauty Gifts

The 30 Day Raw Beauty Queen Experience

The Raw Beauty Queen Lifestyle Program

The Raw Beauty Queen Retreat

———————————

I thank you for reading *Raw Beauty* and I hope that we will meet one day. Until then, go and shine your Raw Beauty into the world!

If this book has nourished you or your life in some way I would love to hear from you.

Please contact me at kemi@keminekvapil.com

WITH THANKS...

To MY MOTHER, the beautiful Ola Olajumoke Baruwa-Ogbeide, for bringing me into the world and wanting only the best for me, and for the relationship we now cherish.

To my father, Mudashir Adeyemi Okanlawon Atanda Baruwa, who left too soon but told me to follow my dreams.

To my first foster parents, Mummy Olive and Daddy Brian, who taught me the power of a connected family where joy, love, food and country and western music were always at hand.

To the foster parents in between, who I have no memory of, but thank you for the bed, food and shelter.

To Mum and Dad Brissenden, who taught me to play and play and play.

To Sue and Russell Price, who gave me one of the biggest gifts of my life – choice.

To Cheryl and Michael Nekvapil, for opening your hearts and home to me as I fostered myself to you at 28.

To my sister Nike, who travelled the journey alongside me, and still does.

To my siblings Zainab, Hazanat, Moriam, Rihannat, Bologi, Elo and Teslin.

To the many women who have raised me higher, held me, inspired me, loved me, believed in me and pushed me forward, including Mrs Molly Reardon, Tatijana Shoan, Sunetra Sarker, Jo Martin, Jo Weakly, Jessica Carney, Joanne Scott, Gisella Torres, Mary Miller, Rowena Love, Sue Grau, Claire Bowditch, Angela Gioffre, Lisa Pearson, Kathleen Foley, Lisa Sullivan, Leanne Knowles, Sharon Vanderhost,

Carly Shrever, Liz Bennett, Debra Ojumu, Kylie Patterson, Michelle Conder, Lola Berry, Kate Allen, Jules Taylor, Lisa Thompson, Sophia Simos, Suzanne Acteson and Samantha Gash.

To the men – Kevin Taylor, Tony Dawes, Paul Tate, Matthew Allen, Abubakar Uyi Ogbeide and the angel who ran the children's home.

To my coaches and mentors.

To Benjamin and Ella, for being who you are. Thank you for choosing me as your mummy, I love you.

To Emrys, for loving me, allowing me to heal, believing in me, nourishing me and, twice a year, making me laugh.

To Lucy, my editor, for your skill, insights, and beautiful generosity.

To me, for having the courage to continually step into myself so that I can step up, step out and make a difference.

Finally, to you, the reader of this book, for getting in touch with your Raw Beauty and sharing it with the world.

ABOUT THE AUTHOR

Kemi Nekvapil has a passion for women fulfilling their full potential, not only for themselves but for each other, too.

As a speaker and wellness coach, Kemi has been in the food and well-being industry for 20 years.

Kemi was an actor, who had leading roles on UK TV and did seasons with both The Royal Shakespeare Company and the National Theatre.

She left acting, when she realised it was not her passion, and became a professional chef, working in London's first certified organic restaurant. She knows good food and the power it has for our bodies, but also for our minds and our experience of life.

She trained in India as a yoga teacher and has been practising yoga for over two decades.

Since moving from the UK, Kemi has pioneered raw food in Australia. She has worked with some of Australia's most highly respected chefs, and she has brought raw food into the mainstream, making it accessible to thousands of people through her business, Kemi's Raw Kitchen.

Kemi has regularly appeared and spoken on TV, radio, print and online media in Australia and overseas, and is also a keynote speaker for forward-thinking global companies.

Kemi's Raw Kitchen led to Raw Beauty Queen, where Kemi channels her passion and purpose to empower self-love and self-worth in women.

She inspires women to add more self-nourishment to their lives by enhancing their eating habits and lifestyle decisions so they can find their passion and live it.

Kemi regularly runs Raw Beauty Queen events, retreats and coaching programs where women's lives are completely transformed by The 7 Principles of Raw Beauty.

Kemi is committed to being part of a world where women nourish themselves and each other to create lives that make a difference.

She lives in Melbourne, Australia, with her husband and two children.

She is a passionate runner, yogi, organic gardener, traveller, weightlifter, homemaker and ice cream lover.

Printed in Australia
AUOC02n0803141014
263747AU00001B/1/P